6-77-63

Statistics

OPUS 25   *Oxford Paperbacks University Series*

L. H. C. TIPPETT

Statistics

Third Edition

London
OXFORD UNIVERSITY PRESS
New York   Toronto
1968

Oxford University Press, Ely House, London W.1
GLASGOW NEW YORK TORONTO MELBOURNE WELLINGTON
CAPE TOWN SALISBURY IBADAN NAIROBI LUSAKA ADDIS ABABA
BOMBAY CALCUTTA MADRAS KARACHI LAHORE DACCA
KUALA LUMPUR HONG KONG TOKYO

First edition in the Home University Library *1943*
Reprinted 1944, 1945, 1947, 1950, and 1952
Second edition 1956
Reprinted 1958 and 1961
Third edition in Oxford Paperbacks University Series *1968*

PRINTED IN GREAT BRITAIN

Contents

Note to the Second Edition

THE FIRST EDITION of this book was written during the early years of the war and described things mostly as they were up to 1939. During the war there were considerable developments in the uses of statistics, in the statistical apparatus of the State, and in statistical techniques, and these have continued. This edition has been revised to take account of these developments and to describe things as they are today; and much of the original illustrative material has been replaced by more up-to-date material. The general scope of the book remains unchanged.

L. H. C. T.

September 1955

Note to the Third Edition

AGAIN I have brought the book up to date, without altering its general character. Much of the illustrative material is new, but some of the old examples, especially of the misuse of statistics, remain. Could it be that such misuse is less prevalent than it was?

L. H. C. T.

June 1967

1
Introduction

STATISTICS AFFECTS EVERYBODY, and touches life at many points. As citizens we help to provide statistical information—our very entry into the world and exit from it are recorded statistically—and propagandists daily try to convince us of something, or even to fool us, by means of statistical facts and arguments. The running of the community through its institutions of government and business depends very much on statistical information, and this dependence increases as business tends to become concentrated in larger concerns and the government intervenes more and more to plan our economic and social life.

The propagandists, administrators, and business executives who use (and misuse) statistics are fairly numerous; and to them may be added such people as politicians, social students, and social reformers who employ statistical facts and methods to provide a basis for policy. Such facts and methods also have an important place in the development of sociology and economics as sciences; the methods are very important to experimentalists in most branches of biology, and are used by workers in the more exact sciences of physics, chemistry, and engineering. Statistical ideas are at the root of many current theories in biology, physics, and chemistry: indeed, a statistical approach is probably one of the most characteristic features of modern science. Some research in literature and history is statistical. Finally, statistics as a subject is naturally a major interest to the comparatively small body of professional statisticians.

As a result of the many approaches to the subject, the word *statistics* and its associated words *statistical* and *statistician* have various meanings. First we have the dictionary definitions, in which *statistics* refers in the singular to the subject as a whole, and in the plural to numerical data. I shall adopt both usages. To the 'man in the street' statistics are just figures, and he is inclined to think of the statistician as being primarily one who counts the numbers of things. To the economist, used to the qualitative ideas of economic theory, *statistical* is almost synonymous with *quantitative*. To the physicist, *statistical* is the opposite of *individualistic* or *exact*, since to him statistics is a subject that deals, above all things, with groups and probabilities rather than with simple entities and certainties. To the experimental scientist who is used to gaining knowledge by conducting experiments under controlled conditions, statistical methods are those which are employed when accurate experimental control is impracticable or impossible. A large field of application of statistics is economic, and so the statistician is sometimes thought of as a kind of economist. On the other hand, statistical methods are basically mathematical, and many people think of a statistician as something of a mathematician. One might almost say that the mathematician accepts the statistician as an economist, and the economist accepts him as a mathematician. Some cynics think statistical methods so uncritical that one can 'prove' anything by them; and others think they are so critical that they can prove nothing. At the other extreme are those enthusiasts who think that as a means of increasing knowledge the power of statistics is boundless and almost magical. I have seen the word 'statistical' used as a pejorative term to characterize a line of argument the writer does not like. These views, excepting the last, are justifiable but incomplete; and the purpose of this book is to give a complete and (as far as I can make it) balanced view of the whole subject.

There are several general considerations which may profitably be borne in mind when approaching the subject of statistics.

First, it is both a science and an art. It is a science in that its methods are basically systematic and have general application; and an art in that their successful application depends to a considerable degree on the skill and special experience of the statistician, and on his knowledge of the field of application, e.g. economics. Statistical methods are not a kind of automatic machine into which numbers can be put and from which perfect results can be taken. Nevertheless, the subject is not a closed mystery, and I believe that it is not necessary to be a statistician to appreciate the general principles underlying it.

As a science, the statistical method is a part of the general scientific method, and is based on the same fundamental ideas and processes. This point will frequently come up in this book, and suggests one reason why the study of statistics is good educationally. It teaches the scientific method in terms of things of everyday experience, and inculcates a habit of scientific approach to ordinary economic, social, and political problems. It will be seen, however, that statistical methods have their own special features. These arise from the fact that the data are not simple, like those that usually result from a well-designed and well-controlled scientific experiment, but are relatively complex, being the result of a number of causes all operating together without control. Statistics deals with figures that are subject to uncontrolled variation.

Another feature that statistics has in common with other scientific subjects is that it is not finished and complete; it is always developing. Despite its power and essential usefulness, it has limitations and imperfections; but future developments will undoubtedly reduce these.

The scope of the subjects included under statistics is wide; and few, if any, statisticians are expert in all branches. Some specialize in the development of the mathematical theory underlying statistical methods, and are essentially mathematicians. Others are interested in the methods themselves, both elementary and advanced, and in their general application to almost any field, although they often have also some special experience of one field. There are also statisticians who are able to use with confidence only elementary methods —perhaps fairly simple tables, diagrams, and averages—but who have a very wide and deep knowledge of some field of application. As will be seen later, knowledge of this kind is very important, and its use makes the work of such a statistician much more than the mere clerical work of tabulation that it sometimes seems to be. Statisticians in this category specialize, and often are as much economists or sociologists, say, as statisticians. One who is an expert in trade statistics may or may not know much about the statistics of public finance, but he will probably know very little of vital statistics; and an expert in vital statistics who wishes to deal with agricultural statistics, say, may have much to learn and much experience to gain.

2
The Raw Material

THE CONCEPTION OF STATISTICS as having to do with figures is the most popular one for very good reasons. Many of the questions that are the subject of common conversation and controversy require numerical data for their resolution. Trains are more (or less) crowded than buses; the English are better (or worse) patrons of sport than of the arts; women drivers are more (or less) competent than men drivers; and so on. These are the kinds of questions that are argued in newspaper columns, drawing-rooms, common-rooms, and public-houses. The disputants give their various experiences both relevant and irrelevant; one always travels by train and never has to stand; another once had to stand on a train journey but has never stood in the bus; another has his own motor-car and does not use buses or trains, but knows that road transport gives a better (or worse) goods service than the railways; and so the discussion proceeds, and probably leaves everyone at the end with his opinion unchanged. But if someone intervenes with really reliable and cogent numerical information based on a wide experience, the question is settled and the discussion peters out. Much pleasurable conversation takes place in the twilight of part-knowledge and social life would be impoverished if all discussions were ruined by the presentation of facts. But we cannot afford to trifle with important subjects by ill-informed controversy.

General impressions are entirely untrustworthy, for some facts and events strike the imagination more than others and are more easily remembered. For example, if we have a theory that the weather changes with the rising and setting of the moon, we notice the occasions when our theory is borne out and forget those when it is not; and it is only by taking systematic records that we can arrive at the truth of the matter. Even when a general impression is qualitatively correct, it may be quantitatively incorrect. If the morning train to town is occasionally late, we are apt to feel that it is more often late than not, whereas an actual count might show that it is late on only one morning in ten, on the average. For example, it actually happened some years ago that the (then) L.M.S. Railway Company analysed their passenger statistics to show how many journeys of various lengths had been made, and discovered that the loss of short-distance passenger business to road transport had been much less than was supposed and that such business was still of importance to the company. Or again, it was a new discovery, made during World War II from the numerical study of the records, that although more ships were lost through submarine attack in large than in small convoys, the proportion lost was smaller in the larger convoys. The fallibility of methods of estimation short of actual measurement or counting is strikingly illustrated by the fact that estimates, made by different experts before counts had been made, of the number of unemployed in the U.S.A. in 1935 varied between six and fourteen million.

We shall see in later chapters that statistical methods are applied to the results of physical, chemical, and biological experiments and observations, as well as to results obtained in social and economic investigations. The making of observations is usually a major part of a research in an experimental science, and instruction in experimental technique and in the handling of the necessary apparatus forms a large part of the training of the physicist, chemist, and biologist. This is no place for a discussion on such a subject, which belongs properly to books that specialize on the sciences concerned. In social and economic research, and in the provision of economic information for government and business, the collection of the material requires little apparatus beyond a pen or pencil and paper, and no experimental technique; and possibly because of this the subject does not always receive the attention it requires. Considerable knowledge and experience are necessary to know where to go for statistical material, how to ensure its accuracy, and how to interpret its meaning; and since these are matters that are regarded as falling within the scope of statistics, we must consider them at some length.

In order to obtain statistical material we may either go to the records of some public body that collects and publishes statistics as a routine, or make a special survey.

The most important routine collectors and suppliers of statistics are governments. Although English records of imports and exports go back to the thirteenth century, the systematic recording of trade statistics started with the appointment of an Inspector General of Exports and Imports in 1696; another important early milestone was the taking of the first British census of the population in 1801. Since the early years of the nineteenth century the volume and scope of British official statistics have increased enormously and continuously up to the present day. World War II, with its associated controls over all departments of the nation's life and with the need for elaborate statistics to operate the controls, gave a great impetus to this movement.

Government statistics originally arose as a by-product of administrative needs and developed partly in response to them and partly through the influence of individuals who saw further than immediate needs. Since the war there has been a conscious attempt to make British official statistics give a systematic and comprehensive picture of many aspects of national life. In addition to providing 'information needed for the efficient conduct of Government business', the function of the British official statistical service is stated in its pamphlet *Government Statistical Services* to be 'to collect and publish information which will be of use to traders and manufacturers in their own business . . . to provide and analyse information which will be of use to research workers in all fields of enquiry in studying conditions in the United Kingdom; and to assist in keeping the public informed of economic, social and financial conditions'. One has only to examine the two general statistical publications of the government, the *Monthly Digest of Statistics* and the *Annual Abstract of Statistics*, to see the very wide range of subjects covered.

In the United Kingdom the collection of official statistics is decentralized, each substantial department of state having its own statistics section, but there is a Central Statistical Office which has, among others, the duty of co-ordinating this activity, ensuring, as far as it can, that the activities of the separate departments neither overlap nor leave gaps and that common definitions are used for the various statistical quantities and terms. Pains are taken to see that the statistics are at the same time as reliable as is practicable, and published soon after the period to which they refer; and this often involves the publication of provisional figures which are sometimes followed, somewhat irritatingly, by revised figures. Definitions and the limitations of the statistics are carefully stated, often in notes necessarily separated from the tables. Much care is taken in the design and lay-out of the tables and they are regarded as models of what statistical tables should be. British official statistics have improved since before the war, and are improving. Professional users of these statistics outside the government service are appreciative of their scope and quality, but also voice their opinions as to directions in which improvements are desirable. For example, the government service is still unable to produce statistical information soon enough after the period to which it refers to satisfy users.

In addition to the government, other organizations such as municipalities, the nationalized industries, the stock and produce exchanges, and trade associations, regularly produce statistical material, mostly of a commercial character. Some of this information is published by the government, with the official statistics; much of it is reproduced in financial journals and in the 'City' columns of daily newspapers.

In different countries the amount and reliability of the statistical information available vary. The situation in the U.S.A. is much the same qualitatively as that in the U.K. but one has the impression that the extent of statistical activity is greater in the U.S.A. At the other extreme, in some countries the statistical information available is meagre and unreliable; and there are countries in all intermediate grades. In the international sphere the activities of the statistical agencies of the United Nations and its associated organizations—the Food and Agriculture Organization, the World Health Organization, and the United Nations Educational, Scientific, and Cultural Organization—are important in encouraging statistics in the 'developing' countries, organizing training for statisticians in these countries, securing international agreement on the definitions of statistical terms, and publishing international statistics. These international organizations work largely with and through the various national statistical organizations.

Statistical information is given in a 'potted' form in a variety of year-books, but such summaries have their dangers as well as their uses since the tables are often given with very little explanation and there is always a risk that the reader may misinterpret the figures. In addition, statistical and economic journals, notably the

Journal of the Royal Statistical Society, contain many critically prepared digests of statistical information concerning a variety of subjects, and although these do not rank as primary sources, they can often be used by the inexpert with greater confidence than the original unedited figures.

Special surveys for obtaining statistical information are made by governments, unofficial bodies, and private individuals; and in this field the last two have led the way up to World War II. Indeed the chief function of unofficial surveys has been to supply the deficiencies of official statistics. The Manchester Statistical Society and the Statistical Society of London (now the Royal Statistical Society) were founded in 1833 and 1834 with declared objects that included the collection of statistics 'illustrative of the condition of society', and in the early years of these societies this formed a fair proportion of their activities. In 1886, Charles Booth, a London ship-owner and merchant, started his famous and very extensive survey of the conditions of life of the people of London. Because of its comprehensiveness and its statistical character this is regarded as a pioneer work. It has been followed by a very large number of social surveys, in the U.K. and in other countries, notably in the U.S.A. Indeed, until about the middle of the twentieth century most unofficial statistical activity seems to have been concerned with the social condition of the people. Special inquiries are also made to discover the attitudes of people to political matters, and their habits and preferences, such inquiries being usually described as public opinion polls and market surveys.

The complicated analysis to which statistical data are often subjected, and the highly condensed form in which they are summarized as averages, give the final results of an investigation a form and order that often are not obvious in the original figures, and an appearance of accuracy and precision they do not necessarily possess. In contemplating the finished work it is all too easy to forget the raw material from which it is made. Nevertheless, no statistical results can be reached that are not already implicit in the data, and the accuracy of the results depends on that of the data. It therefore behoves anyone who uses statistics to exercise care in obtaining them, and if he is going to use those already published, to examine them carefully for errors and to understand their exact meaning.

In order to do this effectively much knowledge is needed of the way in which the figures are collected, of the circumstances surrounding the facts recorded, and of the kinds of errors that can arise. As a check on accuracy, the results of one inquiry can often be compared with those of another to see that they are reasonably consistent, and the data can also be tested for internal consistency. For example, when vital statistics were first collected in some colonial dependencies in Africa, shortly after World War I, it was found in one instance that more children died under the age of one year than were born. That is an extreme example of internal inconsistency exposing error! The following quotation from B. Seebohm Rowntree's 1941 report on his social survey of York gives a picture of the care and attention which are devoted to this business of the collection of reliable statistics:

Obviously, in making a house-to-house inquiry everything depends upon the skill, tact, and reliability of the investigators. It took some time to discover just the right people, but eventually seven were found, five women and two men, on whose work full reliance could be placed. . . . Moreover, a number of 'check' visits were paid, at random, or to cases that seemed abnormal, and in that way the accuracy of the returns was tested and verified.

Nevertheless, in spite of the care exercised in their collection, statistics are not always accurate and the margin of error is sometimes large. Accuracy can usually be improved if the cost of collection can be increased but in a real world that cannot be done indefinitely, and the possibility of error should be taken into account in using any statistics. In the following paragraphs I give a few examples of sources of error and of the difficulties and pitfalls that exist in the collection and the interpretation of statistical data.

It is obviously wrong to rely heavily on figures that are palpably false. For example, a woman's statement of her age is proverbially unreliable, and data based on income-tax returns are in error to the extent that they are affected by tax evasion. Reliable data on household expenditure are always difficult to obtain—how many housekeepers keep even approximate records of the way in which they distribute their expenditure? Information gained by asking questions on matters that are ill-defined, or matters of opinion, depends somewhat on the way the questions are framed. Market investigators have found, when investigating the reasons why people buy particular brands of goods, that the direct question is not likely to give the true reason, as people do not all indulge in honest self-examination, and those who do may not be honest with the investigator.

Indeed, the person questioned may not have thought about the subject before, so that the result of the inquiry is influenced by the inquiry itself. This must often happen in psychological investigations. Because of this some workers in conducting a social survey ask only questions of fact, and content themselves with such inferences about opinions and preferences as can be made from the answers.

It may have been noticed by some readers that government officials in collecting returns often show what seems to be almost a passion for putting people into classes, unless the data can be given in a well-defined form such as age or place of birth. When registering for military service in World War II, for example, each man had a classification number describing his occupation, and however unusual that occupation may have been it had to be fitted into a class. This is because classification is a fundamental part of the statistical method, as we shall see later, but it is done by the official 'on the spot' because only there is the complete information available which enables an accurate assignment to the appropriate class to be made. Difficulties often arise because of borderline cases. In British censuses householders are required to give the occupation of the members of their households. What is the occupation of a weaver who is temporarily unemployed and is doing odd jobs? And if an unemployed man does some other work temporarily, as he believes, what time must elapse before he is regarded as having left the original industry for good and all?

Uniformity and accuracy can be attained in such instances only if very full and precise definitions are given—arbitrarily if necessary. Such definitions sometimes lead to amusing results. For example, in the British census occupations are listed in great detail and are classified into 'orders', one of which groups together: dancing teacher; lecturing; menagerie, zoo; pavement artist; and street singer. It is only fair to add that this is a miscellaneous order of Other Recreations. Statisticians prefer data that are precise, even if the definitions are arbitrary, to data that are vague. The Metropolitan Police once had a book for recording goods 'suspected stolen', but the instructions as to what to enter in this book were not precise, and there was a tendency to include actual thefts; it was feared that this tendency varied from one district to another and from one time to another, thus destroying the value of the returns. When, in 1932, this book was abolished, and the police had to make up their minds whether or not the goods were stolen, the number of recorded indictable offences in the Metropolitan Police area (not necessarily the number of crimes or indictments) rose from 26,000 in 1931 to 83,000 in 1932.

The reliability of statistical observations depends very much on the way in which they are made as well as on the ease with which the required information can be given. Much information is gathered from returns and questionnaires completed by people who are not interested in statistics—citizens, taxpayers, business-men, farmers, factory managers, public officials, and so on—and it must be recognized that people do not like filling in forms. The farmer is interested in growing and selling crops, and he regards the making of statistical returns as a pestiferous waste of time; even a statistician would probably be impatient if, for the information of another statistician unknown to him, he had to interrupt his work on, say, the world trade in ants' eggs, to make a return of the number of man-hours occupied in the investigation. Therefore it is wise not to rely too much on the conscientiousness of people in completing returns; and to remember that the results are likely to be reasonably reliable only if the questions are few, straightforward, and easy to answer.

Where the required information is complicated or difficult, enumerators or 'field-workers' are usually employed. The enumerators employed in making the population census have very full instructions as to how the census forms should be filled up, and experienced field-workers such as usually conduct social surveys know the snags and are not likely to be misled, so that the figures they obtain are usually fairly accurate.

Although data made up of defined measurements are preferable, the statistician often has to deal with vague quantities that are matters of personal judgement, such as general health and intelligence, and qualities of goods, such as the flavour of a food or the state of creasing of a fabric, that can only be assessed qualitatively. To give estimates of such things any value at all, the observer must be specially careful to standardize and define the basis of his judgements as far as possible, so that he can obtain consistent results that may at least be valid for making comparisons. One important stage in doing this is to divide the quantity into a number of parts, and to give points for the parts separately, adding the points to obtain the final result. School examinations provide an example. The candidate answers a number of questions, each of which is marked separately; and some examiners even subdivide the marks for a question, giving so many for the correctness of the answer, so many for the correctness of the method by which the answer is obtained, so many for the orderly presentation of the argument, and so on. Recent investigations have shown that examinations do not measure attainment with great exactness—a result which shows that even when considerable care is taken, it is difficult to make reliable data that have a subjective basis.

However accurate and self-consistent statistical results may be, they cannot be used safely unless everything is known of the way in which they were obtained and of the real meaning behind the figures. It is not often that all the detail surrounding any body of information is published with the figures, and so things are not always what they seem. For example, British criminal statistics give, not the numbers of crimes committed, but the numbers reported to the police; and the two are very different. The proportion of crimes that become known to the police varies with the kind of crime and from time to time, according to the changing attitude of public opinion to the various crimes; and the statistics can give very misleading impressions of the amount of crime extant.

I have already stated that some of the categories used in describing data may have to be defined arbitrarily. It is necessary to be aware of differences that exist between departments of one government, and between countries, in the definitions they adopt for what is nominally the same quantity. As official statistical activities become more organized such differences become progressively eliminated, but it is not safe to assume that they have disappeared entirely. Those who use statistics in the form of series extending over some time have also to be on their guard lest some change in definition or other basis should break the continuity of the series. For example, the figures published periodically of the numbers of the unemployed include only insured workers registered at the exchanges on certain dates, and these are affected from time to time by legislative changes in the classes of workers who may be insured (e.g. in the age limits) and in the qualifications for unemployment benefit. Statistics of causes of death extending over long periods of time are apt to be affected by changes in medical knowledge and (dare a layman suggest?) fashion causing changes in diagnosis. So important is continuity in recorded statistics that statisticians sometimes prefer an existing, and somewhat unsatisfactory, basis to be maintained rather than suffer changes that may in many ways be improvements;

and they are very insistent that when changes are made, two sets of figures should be obtained for some time, one on the old basis and the other on the new, so that the old series can be joined to the new.

The intelligent interpretation of final statistical results often requires a knowledge of unrecorded circumstances surrounding the events recorded. For example, in an investigation on accidents in naval dockyards it was found some years ago that the *recorded* accident rate among apprentices tended to decrease year by year through their apprenticeship, whereas that among naval artificers tended to increase, although both groups were doing similar work. The explanation of this difference is that the apprentices worked under industrial conditions and lost 'time' and money when away from work because of an accident; the artificers worked under service conditions and did not suffer this loss.

The method of inquiry by sample, which is much used in social work, has its own special difficulties and sources of error; that method will be dealt with in Chapter 6.

To give readers a more concrete and integrated picture of what is involved in the collection of data for a statistical inquiry, I am going here to give some detailed comments on an actual example. The Ministry of Transport published three Reports on Road Accidents occurring in Great Britain in the years 1933, 1935, and 1937, and these contained statistical summaries of a number of details of the accidents; the inquiries that provided the information for these reports are the example. In commenting on the collection of the data, I know nothing of what went on 'behind the scenes', but some information is given in the reports and the rest has been surmised.

Presumably the Ministry hoped that from a statistical summary of the circumstances surrounding road accidents, something would be learnt of the underlying causes, and this purpose, as well as administrative and practical considerations, would be borne in mind when deciding what data to collect. The police in various parts of the country reported the details of the accidents and it was therefore necessary to ask only for such information as such a scattered body of men could give reliably and uniformly. In the earlier Reports, estimates were given of the speeds of the vehicles just prior to the accident, but such estimates were admittedly unreliable and were not given in the 1937 Report. There are also other details that would have been very useful but in the circumstances had to be omitted. Thus, the previous accident and medical history of the drivers would have helped to determine whether medical or psychological fitness had anything to do with the tendency of a driver to become involved in accidents.

Since it is not to be expected that the police would fill in the necessary questionnaires with as much zeal as they give to their ordinary duties, it was desirable to limit the number of questions and not to ask for unnecessary details. The statistician who organized the inquiry had to know enough about traffic conditions to decide which questions were important, and which could be omitted as having little or no importance (e.g. the colour of the vehicle or of the upholstery).

Each accident was reported on a form, thus ensuring that no details were overlooked, and the data were collected uniformly and systematically by the various police officers. Some of the details were definite and required little explanation, e.g. the date, place, and time of the accident and the number of persons killed and injured. Others, such as the apparent immediate cause of the accident, needed careful definition. The police were not asked to record the cause in their own words, but sixty-four possible causes were listed and fully described, and the policeman who reported the accident stated which one of these operated at the accident in question. Thus a basis was provided for grouping the accidents according to apparent cause. Those who described these causes needed a considerable knowledge of road traffic to ensure that the list was exhaustive. Another piece of information asked for was the extent of the injuries to injured persons—whether fatal, serious, or slight, and elaborate instructions were also given for defining this.

The development of the details of an investigation of this kind requires much thought and planning, and only a superman would be able to decide the best methods straight away. It is quite clear, from the changes between the 1933 and the 1937 inquiries in the information sought, that the Ministry officials gained experience as they went along; the 1937 questionnaire and method of inquiry, which are given and described in the corresponding Report, are a result of this experience, and are a good example of the first stage of a well-arranged statistical investigation.

Accuracy and reliability in the data are important because their lack cannot be supplied by elaboration and care in the subsequent statistical treatment. However, as this is an imperfect world, most data are imperfect in some degree and many are very imperfect. Nevertheless, they usually contain some information and so are far from valueless; and it is the statistician's job to make the best he can of them. It is a mistake to think, as some do, that inaccurate or unreliable figures should not be given careful treatment; they may not merit it, but they certainly need it. Indeed, extra care is necessary to allow for the inaccuracies and avoid arriving at false conclusions. Thus the statistician will first do all he can to obtain data that are as precise as possible, and will then apply his methods of analysis to make the best possible use of the figures he obtains.

3
Arranging and Presenting the Material

THE RESULTS OF THE FIRST STAGE of a statistical inquiry are sometimes a few fairly simple figures which can easily be presented and understood without any special treatment; but more often there is an overwhelming mass of data and detail. The first task of the statistician is to reduce these, in the two senses of (a) making less the amount of detail and (b) bringing the data into a form whereby the significant features stand out prominently. The statistician must get out of the situation in which he cannot see the wood for the trees. It is easy to state in general terms how this is done: the unimportant details are decided upon, and the data arranged so as to suppress these and leave the important features clearly expressed. The process is essentially one of summarizing.

In fact, this is already started when the field and scope of the inquiry are chosen. With the whole universe before him, the investigator chooses the subject of, say, the housing conditions of one city at one time, and he ignores as irrelevant everything except a few particular facts for the city, such as the numbers and sizes of houses, their distribution, the numbers and composition of the families living in them, and perhaps the incomes of the families. It is not supposed, of course, that the ignored facts are absolutely unimportant, indeed they may afterwards have to be considered even in relation to the original subject of the investigation. The state of housing in a city may, for instance, later be related to unemployment or to other things that are omitted from the original inquiry because it is impossible to deal with everything at once. But some selection must be made, although this may depend partly on such accidents as the investigator's interest. This process of isolating some small part of the universe for study is common to all scientific investigation.

The first and most important step in the statistical reduction of data is usually to group into one class the items that, for the particular purpose in view, need not be distinguished. When many items are put into several groups in this way they are classified. For example, the *Annual Abstract of Statistics* gives the yearly values of nearly 50 groups of products imported and exported. These figures may be reduced to more manageable proportions, and a broader picture of trade be obtained, by using the official classification into ten broader groups, designated: 0. Food and live animals; 1. Beverages and tobacco; 2. Crude materials inedible; and so on up to 9. Commodities and transactions not classified according to kind. In this scheme no distinction is made between, say, rubber and textile fibres, which come in group 2, or between leather goods and iron and steel, which come in group 6: Manufactured goods classified chiefly by materials. It may be advisable to reduce the number of groups still further by combining some of the ten.

Sometimes the subject falls easily and naturally into a few categories. Thus, if families are grouped according to the number of children, the categories will naturally be 0, 1, 2, 3, etc., children. Frequently, however, the subject is such that the classes have to be created more or less arbitrarily, as for the exports just mentioned. There are three points to be observed in making such classifications.

First, any given body of results can usually be classified in many ways, and the best way will depend on the purposes of the inquiry. If the aim is to relate changes in export trade to changes in employment, the exports might be so grouped as to include coal among manufactured articles, because the coal industry employs a lot of labour. For other inquiries it might be better to group the articles according to industries—fish, coal, iron and steel, textiles, engineering, and so on—or according to the amount of shipping space required per million pounds' worth of the article. One difficulty in the way of using existing published figures is that they are not always classified in a way that is suitable for the particular inquiry. The choice of the basis of classification is not a matter of statistical method, but requires special knowledge of the subject of investigation.

The second point, implicit in the whole idea of classification, is that all items grouped together should, for the purposes of the particular inquiry, be sufficiently alike; that each class should be homogeneous. Table 1 gives a summary of the death rates in the U.K.

TABLE I

Deaths during 1965 of Persons of Various Ages, per 1,000 Persons of Corresponding Age living at the Mid-Year. United Kingdom

Age, years	Death Rate
0–5	4.8
5–10	0.4
10–15	0.4
15–20	0.7
20–25	0.8
25–35	0.9
35–45	2.2
45–55	6.0
55–65	15.9
65–75	38.9
75–85	93.5
85–	212.3
0–1	19.9
1–5	0.8

in 1965, and in the upper part of the table all people in broad age-groups are classed together, first in 5-year groups, and later in decades. The figures given in the lower part of the table show that the 0–5 years group is far from homogeneous, for whereas the average death rate for the group is 4.8, that for the first year of life is 19.9, the rate for ages 1–5 years being only a little higher than that for older children. For general mortality studies, the broader grouping may be sufficient, but for a study of infantile mortality much finer grouping is necessary; and figures are in fact even given separately for the first few months of life, although the death rates used in this connexion are not expressed as in Table 1, but as deaths per 1,000 live births. The death rates for the separate years over 75 are also probably far from uniform, but we are not often interested in studying mortality at these ages and the variation is therefore less important and may usually be ignored.

Lack of homogeneity within the groups may always be detected by examining the figures, as we have done those in Table 1, but the investigator can often decide from his general knowledge what variation is likely to occur, and can adopt a scheme of classification accordingly. Usually, the variation in the whole material is so great and complex that it is impossible to have classes that are perfectly uniform. However, the statistician must classify, and so some variation within classes must usually be tolerated. Skill and experience are necessary to steer safely between the Scylla of having too few broad classes, with much variation within each, and the Charybdis of having too many fine classes, each with very little variation.

Consideration of the third general point about classification modifies in some degree the application of the second. Consider Table 2. According to the full classification given there pedestrians

TABLE 2

Factors contributing to Road Accidents and Numbers of Occasions when these Factors were considered by the Police to be associated with Accidents involving Personal Injury in Great Britain in 1952

Factor	Number	
Motor cycle or motor cyclist	24,652	
Private car or driver	30,962	
Taxi or driver	1,050	80,844
Public service vehicle or driver	5,087	
Goods vehicle or driver	19,093	
Other vehicle or driver (not pedal cycle or cyclist)	3,646	
Pedal cycle or cyclist	36,544	
Pedestrian	44,750	
Passenger	14,507	
Other	16,275	
Total	196,566	

N.B. The total number of accidents was 171,757—more than one factor sometimes contributed to the same accident.

are the most culpable. But pedestrians will feel that it is unfair to lump them together and to subdivide motor vehicles and their drivers in such detail. Agreeing, perhaps, that pedal cycles and cyclists are *sui generis*, they will feel that a truer picture is presented by comparing the eighty thousand contributions to accidents by all motors and drivers with the forty-four thousand contributions by pedestrians. In order to give the correct impression, the classes must be of the same rank, so to speak. It is usually impossible to say what is the correct grouping—probably none is absolutely correct and some are merely better than others for particular purposes—but we should realize that the grouping can affect the impression created by the data.

The most usual way of presenting statistical information is in a table of figures. Early in the nineteenth century there was some controversy between those who preferred to present results in a literary form and those who preferred tables and who were accused of presenting only the 'dry bones'. However, the 'table school' won the day, and it is perhaps an echo of this controversy that the original prospectus of the (then) London Statistical Society declared the aims of the Society 'to confine its attention rigorously to facts—and, as far as it may be found possible, to facts which can be stated numerically and arranged in tables'.

Statistical data are usually presented in tables, even in ordinary newspapers, but some writers still seem to prefer giving their figures in a more literary form. The question may be one of taste and training, but I find the tabular method of expression much clearer. It does not make the figures any less dry to have them strung out in sentences and joined by words and phrases such as 'whereas', 'on the other hand', 'as against', and so on. I am not here criticizing the use of words to point out special features or contrasts shown by results given in tables.

There is an art in arranging a table to present data economically and clearly, and in a way to facilitate any comparisons the reader may be required to make. To be useful, a table must not be very complicated. On the other hand, the data of real life, especially of economic and social life, are relatively complicated and do not readily fall into the statistician's categories. Explanatory notes, often given as footnotes, are the means of reconciling these conflicting considerations. Such notes are irritating, but they are necessary, and should be conscientiously studied.

Diagrams and charts are also much used in presenting statistics, and have a value because even statistical ones give some delight to the eye and add a spark of interest to a paper. Their chief importance, however, is that they give a picture of the broad statistical facts that is more readily taken in than a table. It requires a careful examination of the figures of a table to appreciate their full significance, and great concentration of thought is necessary to keep the general picture in mind while reading the figures in detail. Magnitudes are more easily appreciated and remembered when conveyed to the mind by pictures than by numerical figures. On the other hand, the broad picture given by a diagram is not as exact in detail as that given by a table of figures, and since it is somewhat affected by the way in which the diagram is made, it may even give a misleading impression. There follow a few examples to illustrate these statements and to show how some important types of diagram are read.

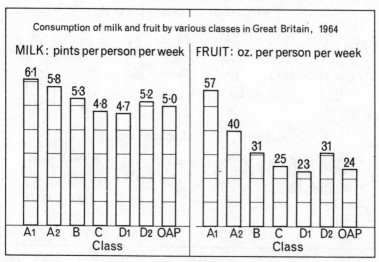

FIG. 1. The classes are defined by the weekly income of the head of the household early in 1964: A1, £39 and over; A2, £24–£39; B, £15–£24; C, £9 10s.–£15; D1, under £9 10s. with one earner or more in the household; D2, as D1 but with no earner; OAP, households mainly dependent on old-age pensions.

Fig. 1 presents the average weekly consumption a head of milk and fruit in Great Britain in 1964, by people in seven groups described as social classes and defined by the income of the head of the household. The actual figures are given, but the quantities are also represented by vertical bars of lengths proportional to the consumptions. From the diagrams it is readily seen that: (1) the

consumption of milk decreases as the class becomes 'lower', except
for the slight rise for class D2 and for old-age pensioners; (2) the
changes in consumption of fruit are similar in general pattern but
larger in proportion. These conclusions are reached from a study of
the figures, but they are not in that way so quickly or vividly im-
pressed on the mind as by looking at the diagram.

Sometimes, instead of the bars of Fig. 1, pictures are used to represent the subjects—bottles of milk or articles of fruit—the number

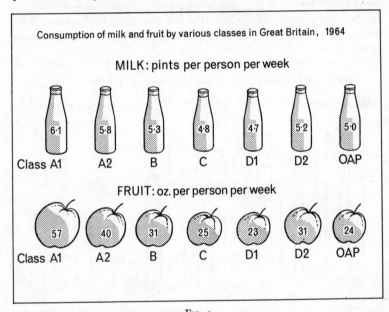

Fig. 2

of pictures equalling the number of units represented. There is something jolly about the presentation of data of manpower by rows of
little dolls. Some serious-minded statisticians are scornful of such
'pictorigrams', but there is nothing unsound about their use;
indeed the use of bottles of milk, etc. in Fig. 1 would prevent such
possible errors as comparing the representations of the quantities
of milk and fruit which are in different units and so are not comparable. I think that there is everything to be said for presenting data
in an attractive and striking way, even by using coloured diagrams

if they can be afforded, although how far pictorial representation should be carried is a question of personal taste. I do not favour some of the very elaborate presentations that can sometimes be seen. Unfortunately, the subject often defies acceptable and plausible pictorial representation. It is difficult to visualize a unit quantity of a vitamin; and much ingenuity would be required to represent the death rates of Table 1 by pictures not too macabre for modern taste.

The data of food consumption may also be used to show how the method of representation can affect the impression created by the diagram. The same data for milk and for fruit are represented in Fig. 2 by milk bottles and apples proportional in *volume* to the quantities consumed. Figs. 1 and 2 present the same facts, but the changes in consumption from class to class are much less striking in Fig. 2 than in Fig. 1. It is better to adopt a method like that used in Fig. 1, where the quantity is represented essentially by a length—a row of pictorial figures would have the same effect—since it is difficult to appreciate quantities by areas or volumes, particularly if the latter are inadequately represented on two-dimensional diagrams.

Sometimes it is desired to show how some quantity is divided into its parts, and this is done by dividing either a column into lengths or a circle into segments. In Fig. 3 both methods are used to show how the aggregated income of people of the United Kingdom for 1964 was derived, and how it was distributed among several broad classes of outlay. The relative magnitudes of the parts can be appreciated at a glance. The choice between the two methods of representation is a matter of taste.

The degree of fluctuation of a quantity apparent from a diagram can be made almost anything we please by choosing the scale of the diagram suitably. Fig. 4 represents a statistical history of a social phenomenon that was a subject of poignant public concern between the two world wars and has remained as a subject of some anxiety— unemployment. Data from the *Annual Abstract of Statistics* have been used to calculate the numbers unemployed at mid-year expressed as percentages of the corresponding numbers of insured workers, and these are represented in the diagram. There are peaks in 1952, 1958, and 1963, and troughs in 1951, 1955–6, and 1961; and the fluctuations seem to be considerable. If, however, we were to present the other side of the picture and present the percentages in employment, the fluctuations would be scarcely discernible on a diagram, drawn on any practicable scale with the zero on the diagram.

The statistician (and the publicist) chooses his scale according to the impression he thinks the figures should convey, and that impression will of course depend on the object for which the figures

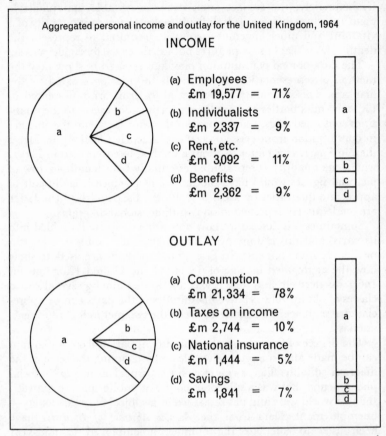

Aggregated personal income and outlay for the United Kingdom, 1964

INCOME

(a) Employees
£m 19,577 = 71%

(b) Individualists
£m 2,337 = 9%

(c) Rent, etc.
£m 3,092 = 11%

(d) Benefits
£m 2,362 = 9%

OUTLAY

(a) Consumption
£m 21,334 = 78%

(b) Taxes on income
£m 2,744 = 10%

(c) National insurance
£m 1,444 = 5%

(d) Savings
£m 1,841 = 7%

Fig. 3. The income of 'employees' includes wages and salaries, pay of the armed forces, and employers' contributions to national insurance, etc. 'Individualists' are professional persons, farmers, other sole traders, and partnerships. 'Rent, etc.' includes rent, dividends, and interest received by persons. 'Benefits' include national insurance benefits and grants from public authorities.

are being used. The honest statistician usually chooses his scale so that the zero value of the quantity being represented appears on the chart as it does at the bottom of Fig. 4; then, the fluctuations are not over-emphasized. But it is not always possible to do this. Sometimes it is legitimate to magnify the fluctuations, and sometimes the zero has no significance, as will be seen in Fig. 7. Nevertheless, the appearance of the zero on the chart is good prima facie evidence of good faith.

Fig. 4 is a typical example of the well-known *time charts* that are used to depict changes in quantities with time, and are so widely understood that even daily papers with mass circulations use them.

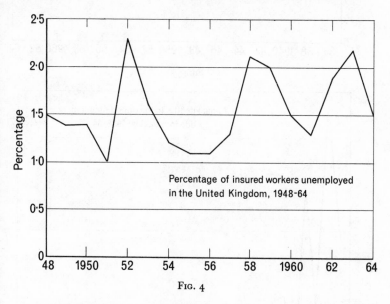

FIG. 4

The detailed examination of a chart, such as we have given to Fig. 4, noting a rise or a fall in level here and there, is a good thing to undertake when there are particular events to which fluctuations can be related; but more often it is desirable to notice the general character of the fluctuations—to obtain a 'bird's-eye view'. There are several patterns to which time fluctuations may conform, although the combination of two or more patterns may make the resulting chart very complicated. However, it is useful to everybody to be able to recognize the various patterns and, where there are several combined, to be able to separate them; accordingly I present

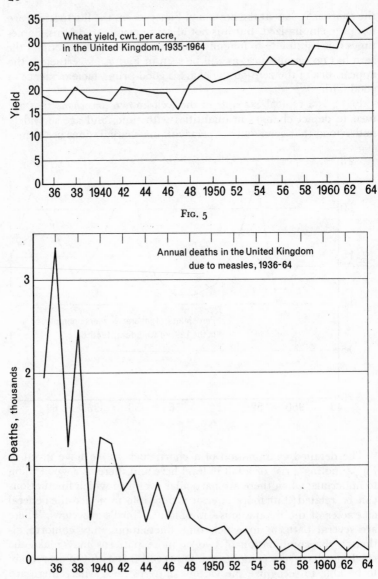

Fig. 5

Fig. 6

in Figs. 5–10 a few illustrations and describe the significant features of the changes they represent.

Fig. 5 shows that the wheat yield per acre fluctuated, year by year, about a fairly level value up to about 1948, but after that there was an upward trend that predominated over the annual fluctuations.

The fluctuations in the deaths due to measles, shown in Fig. 6, are complicated. First, we notice that up to about 1940 the fluctuations are considerable and there is also a strong downward trend. Between about 1940 and 1954 the fluctuations are reduced somewhat, and the downward trend continues, but is less marked. After 1954 the fluctuations are small, and about an unchanging low number of deaths. There is also some tendency for years with large numbers of deaths to alternate with those with small numbers. Up to 1940, the peaks are in the even years; then the pattern becomes disturbed, and thereafter the peaks are in the odd years. Such a pattern, in which the wave-like form of the fluctuations repeats itself at regular intervals (two years in this instance), is described as *periodic*.

Fig. 7, in which monthly mean air temperatures in England and Wales are plotted, exemplifies a periodic variation which is of the particular form known as *seasonal*. Zero temperature does not appear on the chart because the zero on the Fahrenheit scale has no significance, and the physicist's absolute zero is too esoteric for use here. We can note the great extent of the seasonal change compared with the annual fluctuations. Even the exceptionally low temperature of early 1963, which many readers will remember, does not seem to be as important on the diagram as it did when experienced. A change of ten degrees near freezing-point has much greater effects than one of ten degrees in the more temperate zones—an effect which the diagram does not represent. Incidentally, a corresponding diagram of rainfall shows no appreciable seasonal pattern.

Fig. 8, representing the monthly numbers of unfilled vacancies for employment in Great Britain, shows a strong seasonal pattern superimposed on a strong longer-term fluctuation. In each year, the number of vacancies rises to a peak at about mid-year, and falls to a trough at the year-end. The general level rises to high values in 1955, 1961, and 1964, and falls to low values in 1952–3, 1958–9, and 1962–3. (It is interesting to compare Figs. 4 and 8.)

In Fig. 9 are given two time series showing changes over about fifty years preceding World War I in the value a head of the

B

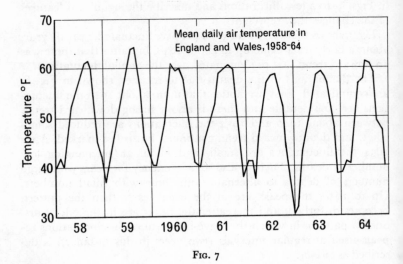

FIG. 7

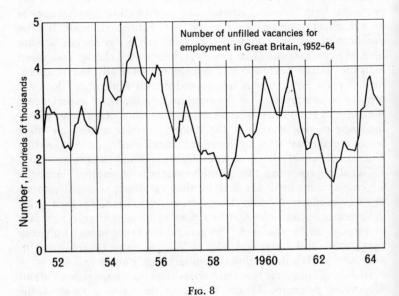

FIG. 8

population of imports into and exports from the United Kingdom, and Sauerbeck's index number of wholesale prices. Sauerbeck's index

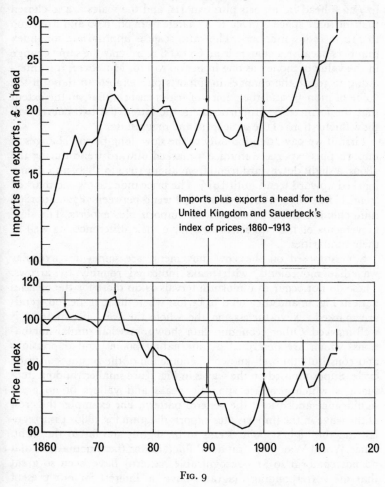

Imports plus exports a head for the United Kingdom and Sauerbeck's index of prices, 1860–1913

Fig. 9

is not much used nowadays, but it has the merit for our present purposes of going back a long time. The two quantities are plotted on a so-called *logarithmic* or *ratio* scale according to which distances in the vertical direction represent proportional changes. Thus, the same space is given to a change from £10 to £11 as to one from £20 to £22 a head in imports plus exports, and the scales are so chosen that the same space is given to a change from 60 to 66 and from 100 to 110 in index numbers. The ratio scale is appropriate for index numbers because a change from 60 to 66 represents the same change in the value of money as one from 100 to 110. Moreover, it is interesting to relate the changes in imports plus exports to those in the value of money; and the choice of scales ensures that, to the extent that the former are proportional to the latter, the two curves will show fluctuations of the same form and magnitude.

First, if we pay attention only to the slow, long-period changes in imports plus exports, we notice a marked upward trend during the 1860s, a slight downward trend from about 1872 to 1896, and then a marked upward trend until 1913. The price index shows no marked trend before 1872, but the downward trend between 1872 and 1896 is much more marked than that for imports plus exports. The slow movements of the two series thus have their differences as well as their similarities.

Superimposed on the slow movements are somewhat irregular wave-like movements, with peaks indicated roughly by arrows. These do not occur at uniform intervals as do those for the measles data in Fig. 6, and they tend to be lost when the long-period trends are marked. Nevertheless, on the whole the wave-like pattern is well marked. Other economic data show somewhat similar fluctuations, which are described as alternating booms and depressions and constitute the well-known phenomenon of the business or trade cycle. Superimposed on the waves in Fig. 9 are smaller random fluctuations which produce sporadic peaks and valleys of no great significance and distort the general pattern. For example, the crest of the wave in the imports plus exports diagram for 1880–4 is irregular and the highest point seems to be slightly too far to the right. Since World War I the 'random' fluctuations (i.e. fluctuations that do not conform to any recognizable pattern) have been so great that the corresponding diagrams have no interest for our present purposes. I shall later discuss the relation between the two series in Fig. 9.

Fig. 10 exemplifies a commonly used form of chart which combines a block diagram such as those in Fig. 3 with a time chart, and may be thought of as a moving block diagram. It shows the yearly

changes in the number of deaths in four broad age-groups in the
United Kingdom. The changes in the number for all ages are
depicted by the changes in the level of the top line, those in the
number for all ages up to 65 years by the changes in the level of the
next lower line, and so on. Changes in the number of deaths in any
age-group are depicted by changes in the width of the corresponding

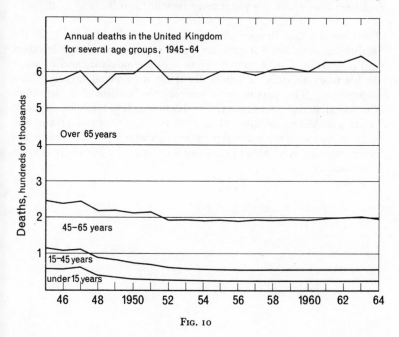

FIG. 10

age band. We see clearly the downward trend in the deaths of children and (from the decreasing width of the age band) in the deaths
of adults aged 15–45 years at least up to 1954. The band for the ages
45–65 years does not change noticeably in width, but there is a
well-marked downward trend in the deaths at all ages up to 65 years
up to 1952. For ages over 65 years the band increases in width—
since all men are mortal it is not surprising that a downward trend
in deaths at ages under 65 is accompanied by an upward trend in
deaths at ages over 65. We notice that the greatest sporadic fluctuations are in the deaths of the old people—presumably old people are

more vulnerable to exceptional climatic and other conditions, and those who succumb in an exceptionally bad year are not available to add to the figures for the next year or two as they might otherwise do. Fig. 10 could be elaborated by dividing the ages into more groups but the resulting graph would be too complicated to apprehend. Complicated graphs of this form are sometimes published, but one wonders how many people receive benefit from looking at them.

Thus we see that in summarizing and presenting his material the statistician classifies it if necessary, and makes use of suitable tables and diagrams. The picture he gives is impressionistic, and he must do his work skilfully and honestly if he is to avoid creating false impressions. The person who receives the statistical information also has an active part to play. For this he needs to know how to read tables and diagrams, and to understand their meaning; and the more he knows of the general principles on which they are made, the more critically is he able to examine them and the less likely is he to be led astray.

4

Some Special Tables and Diagrams of Importance

TABLE 3 GIVES THE WEIGHTS of fifty apples from the same tree. It is typical of a large class of statistical data in that it refers to a number of things of the same kind, varying in some measurable

TABLE 3
Weights of Apples, grams

106	107	76	82	109	107	115	93	187	95
223	125	111	92	86	70	126	68	105	130
139	119	115	128	100	84	129	113	204	111
81	131	75	84	104	110	80	118	186	99
136	123	90	115	98	110	78	82	90	107

character; I propose to show how such figures are dealt with. Usually there are hundreds or even thousands of results in a single collection; there is room here to give only fifty but they will be enough to illustrate the methods.

As they stand, the figures in Table 3 are an almost meaningless jumble, but we can reduce them to order by applying the general methods of classification and summarization mentioned in the last chapter. The weights vary between 68 and 223 grams, and in view of this wide range it is obviously unnecessary to distinguish between apples differing by only a few grams. Even two small boys, faced with such a collection and seeing how different the apples can be, might be satisfied that they were being treated nearly enough alike, if one was given an apple weighing 80 grams and the other one weighing say 90 grams. However, we will be content to regard as equivalent, apples differing by up to 20 grams, make a few broad classes covering the whole range of weights, and count the apples in each class. The results are in Table 4. The *sub-ranges*, as they

Frequency Distribution of Weights of Apples

Weight (grams)	Frequency of Apples
60– 79	5
80– 99	14
100–119	18
120–139	9
140–159	...
160–179	...
180–199	2
200–219	1
220–239	1
Total	50

are called, are in the first column, and the numbers or *frequencies* of apples are in the second column of the table. Table 4 is an example of a *frequency distribution*, so called because it shows how the frequencies of apples are distributed between the various classes of weight. It is a summarized form of Table 3, and in obtaining it we have suppressed little or no detail of any importance even though the classes are very broad.

The two essential elements behind a frequency distribution are the things that are counted, called the *individuals*, and the quantity or quality that is measured and defines the classes, called the *character*. An individual, in the statistical sense, may be a person or a thing; it may be a concrete thing like an apple, or something more abstract like a vote or an experimental observation; and it may be something we ordinarily recognize as a single entity like a man, or a complex entity like a family or a business concern. The character of the apples is called *quantitative* because it is described by a numerical measurement, but *qualitative* characters, which are described in words, are also met with. For example, Table 2 (p. 19) gives a frequency distribution in which the individuals are the 196,566 'occasions' and the character is the factor contributing to the road accident on the occasion. However, for quantitative characters the methods of forming a distribution have been standardized, so that a standard interpretation is possible.

In order to discuss what a frequency distribution really means I shall use an example based on more adequate numbers than fifty. The life of an electric lamp is the number of hours it burns at a standard voltage, and in Table 5 the results for 150 lamps have

TABLE 5

Length of Life of Electric Lamps

(Data by E. S. Pearson, *Journal of the Royal Statistical Society*, **96**, 1933, p. 21)

Life (hours)	Frequency of Lamps
0– 200	1
200– 400	3
400– 600	2
600– 800	10
800–1,000	19
1,000–1,200	21
1,200–1,400	23
1,400–1,600	18
1,600–1,800	17
1,800–2,000	10
2,000–2,200	8
2,200–2,400	5
2,400–2,600	5
2,600–2,800	4
2,800–3,000	2
3,000–3,200	1
3,200–3,400	1
Total	150

been grouped into classes with sub-ranges of 200 hours. For the sake of more vivid representation, this distribution is given as a frequency diagram in Fig. 11, where the lamps in each class are piled in a column proportional in height to the number in the class. These columns are usually represented by plain rectangles, or alternatively the tops of the columns may be joined by sloping lines; I have used the pictorial form here in order to help readers to understand what a frequency diagram is.

In considering a frequency diagram, small irregularities in outline such as the minor peak for the 200–400 hour group in Fig. 11 are ignored, and notice is taken only of the general shape, which is sometimes shown by a smooth curve drawn through the points of an

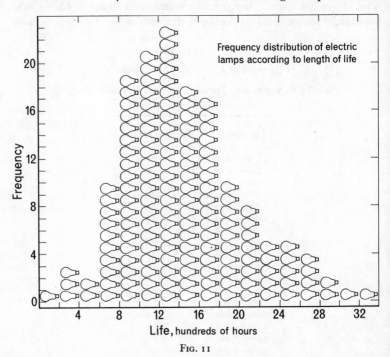

Frequency distribution of electric lamps according to length of life

Life, hundreds of hours

FIG. 11

actual diagram. A diagram of a given general shape means the same thing to statisticians all the world over.

We see that the diagram in Fig. 11 is spread from about 0 to 3,400 hours, showing the extent of the variation in life; that there is a peak, showing a tendency for the lamps to be concentrated about a typical value between 1,200 and 1,400 hours; and that there is a reduction in height towards the sides, showing the comparative rarity of lamps approaching the extremes of life.

In order to see one way in which a frequency distribution can arise, let us imagine a shooting target in the form of vertical stripes instead of the familiar concentric rings, the centre strip being the 'bull', and let us consider a marksman shooting at this many times from a rifle. The shots will be peppered over the target. There will be more shots in the central strip than in any other, and as we move from the centre towards the edges each strip in turn will have fewer and fewer shots, until the extreme strips will have very few indeed, or none. If we count the shots in each strip, and draw a frequency diagram, the shape will be like that just described for the lamps, with a peak at the centre and tailing off towards the edges. I do not suggest that all frequency distributions arise in this kind of way, but this illustration often helps readers to see what a frequency diagram means.

There are two main things to notice about a diagram like Fig. 11, after its general shape; these are the position of its peak and the width of the distribution. The peak for Fig. 11 is in the 1,200–1,400 hour group; if we had another batch of lamps with a peak in, say, the 1,800–2,000 hour group, we should probably prefer those lamps as having a longer typical life. The width of the distribution measures the degree of variation about the typical value. For example, the imagined batch of lamps with a typical life of 1,800–2,000 hours might have a distribution ranging from 0 to 4,500 hours, and this batch would be much more variable in life than the original batch. If we had two marksmen shooting at similar targets of the kind just described, a good marksman and a poor one, the frequency diagram for the good one would be narrow with a tall, sharp peak showing little variability in the placing of the shots; that for the poor marksman would be broad and squat, with more of a knoll than a peak, and showing much variability. This characteristic of variability is a highly important one.

The more or less symmetrical bell-like shape of Fig. 11 is the most common in frequency diagrams, but other shapes do exist, which describe other types of variation. For example, the distribution among the people of the United Kingdom of wealth in most of its forms is such that the vast majority are relatively poor and a very few people are very wealthy; and this distribution is presented by an extremely lop-sided diagram of the kind shown in Fig. 12, which shows the distribution of personal incomes in the United Kingdom as assessed for income tax for the year 1962–63. The uneven distribution of these incomes is even more pronounced than appears in Fig. 12, since if the scale were large enough the diagram would extend with a long thin 'tail' to incomes of over £20,000. This kind of distribution is often given with a finer division of the value scale at·the lower end, as in Fig. 12. This is a complication for the statistician in constructing the diagram and gives rise to the special form of the frequency scale; but the reader need be concerned only with the general outline.

It is sometimes convenient to represent frequencies in so-called *cumulative* diagrams, as is done for the data of Fig. 12 by the full line

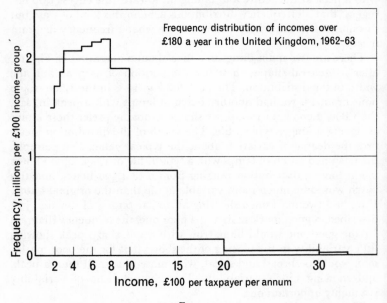

FIG. 12

in Fig. 13, in which percentages of the total frequency are repre-sented. This diagram shows, for example, that 50 per cent of tax-payers had incomes in excess of £720 (as read from the large-scale diagram from which Fig. 13 was constructed) and that about 5 per cent had incomes in excess of £2,000. The cumulative diagram of a distribution of the form of that of Fig. 11 starts almost horizontal and gradually slopes to the kind of steep fall shown in Fig. 13.

If there is interest in showing how the grand total of all incomes is distributed among different classes of taxpayer, a diagram like that shown by the broken line in Fig. 13 is convenient. This shows, for example, that the 5 per cent of taxpayers who had incomes in excess of £2,000 received nearly 15 per cent of the grand total income, and that approximately 50 per cent was received by taxpayers with individual incomes exceeding £1,000, who constituted roughly 25 per cent of the taxpayers.

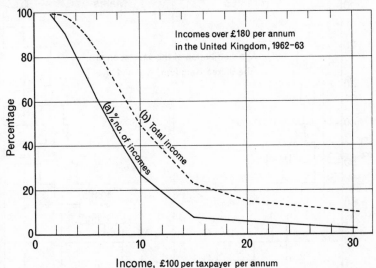

FIG. 13. Incomes in excess of stated amounts per taxpayer per annum related to (a) the percentage number of taxpayers receiving those incomes and (b) the total income of those taxpayers expressed as a percentage of the grand total income of all taxpayers.

Corresponding diagrams to those in Fig. 13 can be made to represent percentages for taxpayers having incomes less than the stated amounts. These appear as Fig. 13 does if turned upside down and viewed in a mirror.

The frequency distribution of the human population classified according to age is sometimes represented in the special form illustrated in Fig. 14. The diagram is turned on its side relative to the other distributions so that the variable, age, is represented vertically, and the frequencies of males and females are represented separately, to the right and left of the base line respectively. In Fig. 14 the broad variations are the same for males and females. In 1961 there is a 'bulge' (perhaps 'pimple' would be a more descriptive term) in the 10–15 year age-group which must be of interest to people like educationists who have to provide for these children as they

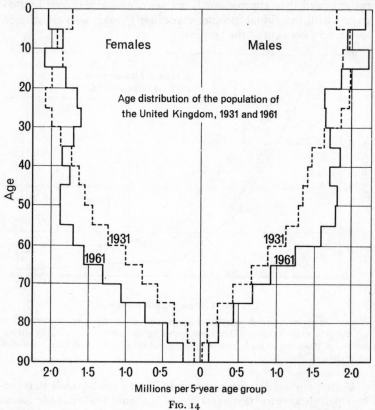

FIG. 14

grow. In contrast to 1931, there is in 1961 a bulge in the 40–60 year age-groups, which will have important effects twenty and thirty years onwards. The numbers in these age-groups are not many fewer than those in the 10–30 year groups thirty years before, in 1931.

A list of the characters of several hundreds of individuals seems to be an overwhelming and chaotic mass of information, particularly if the items are in some irregular order in which they happen to have been recorded. A frequency distribution is an economical summary of such figures, since it replaces the several hundred readings by a table with some ten or twenty entries, and it reduces the

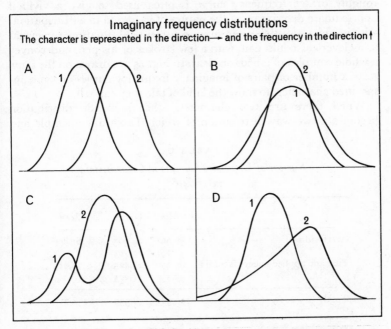

FIG. 15. A. The typical value of 2 is higher than that of 1, but both distributions show the same degree of variation. The overlap of the curves shows that some individuals in 1 have higher values than some in 2.

B. The typical value is approximately the same for 1 as for 2, but 1 shows the greater degree of variation. There are more very high and very low values in 1 than in 2.

C. The distribution 1 shows a mixture of two well-defined types, whereas 2 shows homogeneous variation.

D. The typical value of 2 is higher than that of 1, but the variation in 2 is greater in degree and is asymmetrical in form, so that there are more very low values in 2 than in 1.

chaos to an order the mind can comprehend. Indeed, the things we need to know about such a body of observations are not really many or complex. We need to know whether there is a well-defined typical value of the character, and if so what the value is; to what extent the individuals vary about that type; and whether the variation extends equally above and below the type. These facts are readily seen from and described by a frequency table or diagram. A roughly drawn frequency curve is often used to give a vivid if approximate description of the nature of variation in a distribution; with its aid a statistician can sum up a statistical situation, somewhat as a clever cartoonist can, with a few strokes of his pen, and convey a whole complex of moods or ideas. In Fig. 15 are drawn on the same scale a number of pairs of imaginary frequency curves of some unspecified character, to show the kind of tale they can tell.

When there are two characters, the frequency distribution becomes a two-way distribution of which Table 6 is a simple and

TABLE 6

Number of University Students in Great Britain in 1964/65

	Men	Women	Total
Arts faculties	36,991	24,905	61,896
	44,791	*17,105*	
Pure and applied science faculties	63,390	13,425	76,815
	55,590	*21,225*	
Total	100,381	38,330	138,711

Data from the *Annual Abstract of Statistics*. The figures in italics are calculated figures and are explained in the text.

commonly occurring example. The 138,711 students are characterized by (*a*) their sex and (*b*) the type of faculty; and the number with each combination of characters is given in the body of the table (ignore for the time the numbers in italics). We note from the totals in the margins that there are more men than women students, and more science than arts students. It may be interesting also to note from the body of the table that there are more men than women students in each group of faculties, and that there are more science men than arts men but fewer science women than arts women. We may ask, further, whether the tendency to take science rather than arts is greater or less among the men than among women, or, alternatively, whether the tendency for students to be men rather than women is greater or less among arts than among science students. These two questions are, as we shall see, alternative forms of the same question. The totals in the margins are irrelevant to the question—we must examine the figures in the body of the table, and examine them not individually but as a whole.

TABLE 7

Percentages of University Students

	Men	Women	Both Sexes
Arts faculties	37	65	45
Science faculties	63	35	55
All faculties	100	100	100

One way of eliminating the total numbers of men and women is to express the frequencies as percentages of their respective totals; this has been done in Table 7. Now we see a strong tendency for men to be science students and for women to be arts students. The second form of the question is answered by taking percentages

TABLE 7*a*

Percentages of University Students

	Men	Women	Both Sexes
Arts faculties	60	40	100
Science faculties	82	18	100
All faculties	72	28	100

of the faculty totals as in Table 7*a*. From this table we see that although there are more men than women in both groups of faculties, the proportion of men is greater among science than among arts students.

These two approaches to the question may be combined into a single approach by calculating what frequencies would be expected in the body of Table 6 if the tendencies postulated in the question were absent—if, given the totals in the margins, chance alone decided the distribution among the four places in the body of the table. These expected frequencies are given in italics in Table 6. They are calculated so that 44,791 ÷ 100,381 and 17,105 ÷ 38,330 and 61,896 ÷ 138,711 are all equal; 44,791 ÷ 61,896 and 55,590 ÷ 76,815 and 100,381 ÷ 138,711 are all equal; and so on. The italic figures in Table 6 can be compared with the corresponding arabic figures, and it should be noticed that the difference is the same for all four comparisons, namely, 7,800; in two instances, diagonally placed, the italic figures are in excess, in the other two the arabic figures are in excess. The difference shows that the distribution in the body of the table is not a chance distribution, and we may briefly sum up the result by saying that there is a tendency for the quality of 'maleness' to go with a preference for science in choosing a university course and, conversely, for the quality of 'femaleness' to go with a preference for arts.

In statistical language, we say that sex and the type of faculty of study are *associated* or that there is an *association* between sex and type of faculty. Had the actual frequencies been those given in italics in Table 6 we would have said that sex and type of faculty are *independent*. A two-way table with qualitative characters such as Table 6 without the italic figures, is termed a *contingency table*.

Besides the fact of association, we have to note its sense or direction (that 'maleness' and science go together rather than 'maleness' and arts), and its *strength*. The actual frequencies in Table 6 differ markedly from the chance frequencies given in italics and so the association is fairly strong. Had the actual frequencies followed the pattern

23,566   38,330
76,815   0

the association would have been stronger. Had all the men been scientists and all the women arts students it would have been at its strongest (the totals in Table 6 would then have been different). The strength of association may be of any degree between something little greater than that for independence and the strongest association in which the value of one character (male or female in our example) completely determines the value of the other (whether arts or science).

Contingency tables may have more than two rows and columns, but the interpretation of manifold tables with qualitative characters is sometimes complicated. When the characters are quantitatively expressed, the table, known as a *correlation table*, often discloses a relatively simple pattern that renders interpretation relatively easy. Tables 8 and 9 are examples.

TABLE 8

Numbers of Husbands and Wives of Various Ages residing together on the Night of the Census, 1901, thousands

(Data from *An Introduction to the Theory of Statistics*, by G. U. Yule, 1922)

| | | | | Age of Wife | | | | | |
	15–25	25–35	35–45	45–55	55–65	65–75	75–85	85–	Total
Age of Husband									
15–25	193	50	1	...	...	...	...	...	244
25–35	231	1,162	108	4	...	...	...	...	1,505
35–45	12	408	977	92	4	...	...	...	1,493
45–55	1	36	320	652	66	3	...	...	1,078
55–65	...	5	37	211	358	34	1	...	646
65–75	...	1	6	24	105	133	10	...	279
75–85	...	...	1	4	10	30	22	1	68
85–	...	...	...	...	...	2	2	...	4
Total	437	1,662	1,450	987	543	202	35	1	5,317

The individuals of Table 8 are married couples living together on the census night of 1901, and the characters are the ages of husband and wife. There is a pronounced association which is shown by the tendency for all the frequencies to occur in cells about one diagonal, and this gives the whole table a characteristic appearance.

Association between two quantitative characters is called *correlation*, and we say that the two characters are *correlated*. The strong correlation between age of husband and wife is in accordance with our general experience, for although men sometimes have wives much younger than themselves and, less often, wives much older than themselves, age in the husband is usually associated with age in the wife.

If, however, we consider the ages at which husbands and wives die, the correlation largely disappears. Whether the wife dies when young or old makes little difference to the age at which the husband dies. This lack of correlation is shown by the appearance of Table 9, which refers to married couples whose ages at death were recorded on the gravestones of country churchyards in the Yorkshire dales.

TABLE 9

Numbers of Husbands and Wives who died at Various Ages

(Data from gravestones in the Yorkshire dales; *Biometrika*, **2**, 1903, p. 481)

				Age of Wife						
	15–25	25–35	35–45	45–55	55–65	65–75	75–85	85–90	95–	Total
Age of Husband										
25–35	2	4	4	5	...	5	2	...	...	22
35–45	...	7	5	4	11	12	7	1	1	48
45–55	...	4	9	7	11	17	28	6	...	82
55–65	...	6	13	17	33	35	32	9	1	146
65–75	1	11	23	18	45	74	64	19	3	258
75–85	3	6	14	17	27	71	81	28	1	248
85–95	...	1	3	7	9	13	21	12	...	66
95–	...	...	...	1	2	...	2	...	1	6
Total	6	39	71	76	138	227	237	75	7	876

Table 9 looks quite different from Table 8 in that the frequencies do not tend to be concentrated about a diagonal, although statistical analysis shows that there is a slight tendency for this to occur and that there is consequently a very weak correlation.

When the number of individuals is small, correlations may be shown to the eye by a *correlation diagram*, as exemplified in Figs. 16A and B. The individuals are the thirty years from 1935 to 1964, and for Fig. 16A the characters are the total wheat crop and the area culti-vated under wheat each year. In the diagram, the position of each dot represents for a year the crop and the acreage. In Fig. 16B the crop is similarly plotted against the yield per acre. Both diagrams show a correlation by the fact that the points tend to be clustered about a diagonal, although there are some marked deviations. On the whole the clustering is somewhat closer in Fig. 16B, indicating that over the thirty years yield per acre had a closer correlation than area planted with the variations in the crop. In the second edition of this book, dealing with the eighteen years up to 1952, the correlation with area was the closer—the large increase in yield per acre since 1948, shown in Fig. 5 (p. 26), has altered the picture. Care is necessary in generalizing from data in which there are changes in time.

This conception of correlation was introduced by Galton late in the nineteenth century, and it is now one of the most important

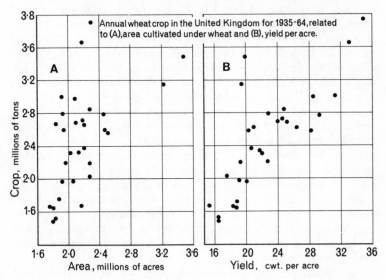

Fig. 16

and useful ideas we have. Correlation expresses the general idea of a relationship between two quantitative characters and also of departure from that relationship—of a relationship which is apparent and well defined when there is a number of observations, but which describes only approximately the connexion between the two characters for any one individual.

When the two characters tend to increase together, the correlation is said to be *positive*, and when one tends to increase as the other decreases, the correlation is *negative*. In a table or diagram a positive correlation gives the same appearance of clustering as a negative one, but the figures or points tend to follow the other diagonal. The correlations in Table 8 and Figs. 16A and B are all positive, and it is perhaps unfortunate that the rules for arranging tables and diagrams should be such that the table shows a 'down-hill' trend, moving from left to right, and the diagram an 'up-hill' trend for positive correlation.

We may interpret correlation by imagining that we have taken a man at random, and that we wish to guess or 'predict' his age. If we know nothing about him except that he is one of those recorded in Table 8, we can only say that he is somewhere between 15 and about 90 and that he is most likely to be near the typical age-group of 25–35. If, however, we are told that his wife is between 25 and 35, we see from Table 8 that he will be between 15 and 75. The effect of the correlation is to reduce the range of uncertainty of our prediction. In Table 9, on the other hand, the range of uncertainty of prediction is from 25 to something over 95, if we know only that the man's age is recorded on a gravestone in the Yorkshire Dales; and if we also know that his wife died between 65 and 75 years of age, say, the range of uncertainty is only very slightly reduced. The stronger the correlation, the greater is the accuracy with which a knowledge of one character enables us to predict the value of the other, as compared with the accuracy of the random guess.

Often it is desired to derive a formula by means of which one variable may be predicted from the value of another. This process is called *regression analysis* and the formula a *regression equation* or *line*. A regression equation shows how, on the average, one quantity changes with the other.

Figs. 16A and B suggest another interpretation of correlation which is only sometimes valid. It is common sense that the crop will tend to increase with the area cultivated and with the yield per acre; these two factors may be regarded as 'causes' of the crop variation, and the correlation as a visible demonstration of their operation. This leads us to an interpretation of the scatter of the points. Had the cultivated area been the only causal factor that varied between 1935 and 1964 all the points in Fig. 16A would have been accurately *on* a line sloping diagonally. The scatter is due to the operation of some additional cause or causes, which our common sense tells us can, in this instance, only be those affecting the yield per acre. Similarly, the trend of points in Fig. 16B is due to the causes associated with the yield per acre, and the scatter to the disturbing causes associated with the area cultivated. If the correlation is high, the cause accounted for is relatively important and the disturbing causes are relatively unimportant. A lower degree of correlation may be interpreted to mean that the causes of which account is taken are less important than the unaccounted causes. The results of Figs 16A and B are incidentally of interest since the causes affecting the changes in cultivated area are mostly economic and political, and those affecting the yield per acre are meteorological and technical. In the years 1935–52, as was shown in the second edition of this book, although both sets of causes produced variations in the total crop of wheat, variations due to economic and political causes were more important than those due to technical causes and the weather. Later the (presumably technical) effects of yield per acre have predominated.

Thus we see that when any cause affects the variations in a character, the effect shows itself as a correlation. But the existence of a correlation does not prove the existence of a causal relationship. Two characters can be correlated because they are both affected by a third group of causes, and sometimes they may simply happen to be correlated. Finally, I emphasize the fact that a correlation, like all statistical results, merely describes the relations within a given set of data, referring to a particular set of conditions and taken at a particular time, as has been illustrated for the wheat crops. It may or may not be possible to generalize from such results.

Correlation may show itself in most complicated ways when the two characters are in a time series. Then, the best representation is in a time chart like Fig. 9 (p. 29), and it is necessary to consider separately the different features of the time variations. For example, up to about 1900 the slow movements in imports plus exports and prices are different, and as far as these movements are concerned the correlation is low. For the wave-like fluctuations, on the other hand, the peaks for the two series tend more or less to coincide, and these shorter-term movements show a fairly strong positive correlation. It is not my concern to explain the data of Fig. 9, but it may help readers to regard them in the following way. We may think of a *volume* of foreign trade, consisting of quantities of goods imported and exported, the movements of which may be represented by dividing the *value* of imports plus exports a head by the index number and multiplying by one hundred, thus correcting that value to constant prices. This measure of volume rose fairly steadily until 1890, and after an intermission between 1890 and 1900, there was a further fairly steady increase from 1900 to 1913. There were a few fluctuations about these trends but they were not very large, and the wave-like movement, although showing signs of its presence, was not well marked. Substantially, the whole period was one of an expanding volume of foreign trade relative to the size of the population. Prices showed the movements already described partly because of fluctuations in trade generally and partly because of the special monetary influences of the demand for and supply of gold. It was the impact of these price fluctuations on the expanding volume of foreign trade that produced the pattern of fluctuations in the value of imports plus exports a head shown in Fig. 9.

Generally, a correlation between time series that arises from two similar trends is seldom due to a causal relationship; one that results from similar cyclical movements is sometimes due to a causal relationship; and one that results from correlated random movements is often due to a causal relationship. There are, of course, methods of statistical analysis that enable the various kinds of fluctuations and correlations to be separated out and measured more exactly than we can do by a cursory examination of the diagrams. These form a very large subject known as *The Analysis of Time Series*.

Frequency distributions of single characters give rise to the concept of variation about a type, and tables and diagrams relating pairs of characters to the concepts of association and correlation. These concepts are essential to the statistician but they are also useful to the ordinary citizen, since they help in making sense of figures that come within everyday experience.

5

'Expressing it in Numbers'

ON A WALL of the Biometric Laboratory at University College, London, where much of the present science of statistics has been developed, was once written the following motto:

When you can measure what you are speaking about and express it in numbers, you know something about it, but when you cannot measure it, when you cannot express it in numbers, your knowledge is of a meagre and unsatisfactory kind.—LORD KELVIN

This motto well expresses the spirit that has inspired statisticians, and much of the work of the pioneers of the subject has been towards developing ways of expressing in numbers measures of statistical concepts which I have so far described only in general terms. I think the motto is an overstatement, since good has come of many qualitative studies—in biology for example—and it omits to state the requirement that the numerical measure should be of a kind that can be brought into a system and related to other quantities, or it is sterile and little better than qualitative knowledge. All the same, the development of numerical measures is a very important step in any science, and in this chapter I describe some of the chief measures in statistics. The use of these measures carries still further the process of summarizing data, bringing into prominence and describing the few features that are of most significance.

The simplest statistical quantities are rates, ratios, and percentages. It is not necessary for me to define these here, for we are taught in the arithmetic lesson at school how to calculate them, but I point out one fundamental feature they have in common: they all express the value of one quantity relative to another. A death rate

expresses the number of deaths in a locality during a year relative
to the number of people living in that locality; and the percentages
of unemployed workers are relative to the numbers of insured
workers.

One purpose in using a method of expression is to help people to
grasp the meaning of the figures; to bring them home to the imagination. In common with most people I have very little occasion to
consider the populations of towns and countries, and so when I
read in 1954 that the population of Hong Kong was one and three-
quarter millions, my imagination was unstirred. Some people try to
present facts of this kind by some such device as suggesting that
1,750,000 people stood shoulder to shoulder would reach from London to Edinburgh. This does not help me in the least. But I know
Liverpool and that it has a population of about three-quarters of a
million; when I realized that the population of Hong Kong was about
two and a third times this figure I began to have some conception of
what that was.

One of the jobs of the statistician is to find suitable standards of
reference. Note however that the standards should be *suitable*.
I remember, a few years before World War II, hearing the Chancellor of the Exchequer expounding his budget over the wireless
and emphasizing its enormous total—some eight hundred million
pounds. To those of us who only handle a few hundred pounds of
money in a year such figures mean only a tremendous amount of
money. Had the Chancellor expressed the total as amounting to a
rate of about £20 a head of the population, our comprehension
would have been a little better, although the impression gained by a
man with a family income of £100 a year would have been different
from that gained by a £20,000 a year man. I think the Chancellor
would have done best to have expressed the amount of the budget
as a ratio of the national income at that time—roughly one-fifth.

A second reason for expressing a quantity as a ratio or percentage
of another is that the ratio may contain all the information that
matters, actual values of the two quantities being irrelevant details.
For example, if we wished to compare the risk of death in two localities, it would be misleading to compare the numbers of deaths, as the
populations in the localities might be different, and the sizes of the
populations are irrelevant. All the information we would need is
contained in the death rates.

Percentages are much used when it is desired to study the relative changes in some quantity with time without considering the absolute amounts of the quantity or the changes. Then the value of the quantity at some given time or *base* is taken as a standard of reference, and the values at other times are expressed as percentages of this. Such percentages are *index numbers*. The changes in prices in Fig. 9 (p. 29) are described as index numbers with the average for the decade 1867–77 as a base.

Index numbers are very useful for comparing changes in quantities that differ in kind. For example, in Fig. 9 the imports plus exports a head could have been expressed as percentages of the average value for 1867–77 and so have been directly compared with the index numbers of prices; index numbers of wages and prices are often compared in formulating or combating claims for increased wages; and rough impressions of changes in industrial productivity are obtained by comparing indexes of industrial production and of the numbers of people employed. Such comparisons can be considerably affected by the choice of the base year or years. If, for example, a base year is chosen in which, say, prices were abnormally low and wages were not, this will tend to increase the subsequent indexes of prices more than those of wages; a superficial comparison of the index numbers involves the tacit assumption that prices and wages were correctly related in the base year—which may or may not be the case.

Some rates or ratios devised for special purposes, particularly those used in population and vital statistics, are very complicated. For example, in studying population trends, a net 'reproduction rate' is calculated from (*a*) the numbers of girls born in a given period, (*b*) the numbers and ages of the mothers, and (*c*) the proportions of the girls that will live to the various ages when they may themselves become mothers. This ratio is so calculated that if it is 1.0 the population is just maintaining its supply of producers of children—i.e. potential mothers. For England and Wales the effective rate was about 0.8 during the years shortly preceding World War II, but since the war it has fluctuated about 1.0.

Often, the investigator has little difficulty in devising a reasonably suitable rate, ratio, or percentage for his purpose. For example, an important factor in the causation of deaths due to road accidents is the number of motors on the roads—the number of lethal instruments abroad. Indeed, one would expect that if everything else remained constant, deaths would vary proportionately with the number of motors, so that variations in the ratio of the number of deaths to the number of motors would indicate the effects of variations in the other factors. However, we do not know the number of motors on the road, but the average number of licences current each year provides a good, if rough, measure, the use of which involves classing variations in the annual mileage of the average car among the 'other factors'. Thus, a rate that may reasonably be regarded as indicating the effect of these 'other factors' is the number of deaths per 1,000 current motor licences. A few values of this rate are given in Table 10. The lower values since World War II and the down-

TABLE 10

Number of Deaths due to Road Accidents per 1,000 Current Motor Licences in Great Britain

Year	Deaths
1938	2.2
1945–49	1.4
1950–54	1.0
1955–59	0.8
1960–65	0.7

ward tendency are perhaps some slight consolation for the distressing increases in the actual numbers killed.

Sometimes it passes the wit of man to devise a suitable rate or ratio. In 1938 there were 253 fatal road accidents in Lancashire and 88 in Derbyshire. Does this mean that Lancashire drivers were worse than those in Derbyshire? Not necessarily. The two counties differ in population, in numbers of motors on the roads, and in the length and character of the roads (i.e. in ratio of rural to urban mileage); and I do not know how to devise a rate that will properly take account of these factors and measure the relative standards of driving in the two counties.

A ratio or a percentage is not always the best means of comparing two quantities; a simple difference is sometimes better. A difference in aeroplane speed of say 25 miles per hour is $12\frac{1}{2}$ per cent of 200 m.p.h. and only about 8 per cent of 300 m.p.h., but such a difference is equally important to a bomber trying to outstrip a fighter at both speeds. (This sentence was written before the advent of jet engines.)

Rates, ratios, and percentages are rather tricky quantities to deal with, and the unwary sometimes go astray in using them. Most of the errors are due to a neglect of the fact that these quantities are made up of a numerator and a denominator. For example, the percentage of all insured workers that are unemployed is:

$$\frac{\text{number of insured workers unemployed}}{\text{total number of insured workers}} \times 100.$$

We call this, shortly, the 'percentage unemployment' and so are apt to overlook the denominator, which does not appear in the short title of the quantity. I give a few examples to illustrate this point.

TABLE II

Deaths per 1,000 Live Births in Urban and Rural Areas, at Various Ages

	Deaths under One Month	*Deaths under One Year*	*Deaths under One Month as Percentage of Deaths under One Year*
Urban	29.67	95.37	31
Rural	23.77	58.66	40

The error of thinking that a large percentage change in a quantity necessarily means a large actual change is less commonly made than it was, and when the Minister for the Production of This or That bids us rejoice because the output of this or that has increased by five hundred per cent, even those of us who are not statisticians sceptically ask, 'Five hundred per cent of how much?'

Changes in a percentage may be due to changes in the numerator, in the denominator, or in both; or the changes in the numerator and denominator may compensate for each other to keep the percentage unchanged. Thus, the percentage of the insured workers in employment in 1927 was about the same as in 1937, viz. about 90 per cent; but the estimated numbers of insured workers in employment increased from about nine and three-quarter millions in 1927 to rather more than eleven millions in 1937. As another example, suppose that a quantity has decreased by 20 per cent from 100 to 80, and that subsequently it increases by 20 per cent of the new value— i.e. by 16. The original value is not restored.

The following example is given by Sir Austin Bradford Hill. The data of Table 11 were used by someone to show the bad effect on the infantile death rate in rural districts of the lack of facilities for dealing with confinements. To this lack was attributed the higher percentage deaths under one month in the rural areas given in the last column of Table 11. In fact, as Sir Austin points out, the death rate under one month of age is lower in rural than in urban areas, and the relatively unfavourable percentage for the rural areas is due to the relatively favourable death rate for all ages under one year, i.e. to the reduction in the denominator of the percentage. A lack of facilities in rural areas may account for some infantile deaths, but the figures of Table 11 do not show such an effect.

Before leaving the subject of percentages, I wish to protest against the grandiloquent misuse of the term percentage when a simple ratio would be better. When a ratio is an awkward fraction, it is convenient and legitimate to multiply it by one hundred and convert it to a percentage; 'seven per cent' is a better phrase than 'seven hundredths'. When, however, the ratio is a multiple of unity, it is pretentious to express it as a percentage; it sounds very grand to talk of an increase of five hundred per cent, but it is better English to talk of an increase to six times the original value. Worst of all is a mixture of methods of expression. The mixture is rich in the following extract from a letter to a newspaper printed some years ago, even if we allow that the lack of intelligibility of the last sentence is due to the omission of a £ sign before the last figure:

As far as British cycles are concerned, the best illustration is that of comparison with Germany, whose exports have fallen in the last few years to under 200,000, whereas during the same period British exports have increased to approaching 400,000, and in the recent trade depression while Germany has lost nearly 60 per cent of her exports Great Britain has lost but 36 per cent. ... So, too, the importance of reciprocal arrangements in the Dominions may best be emphasized by the fact that, whereas in 1929 our exports to the self-governing Dominions and India amounted to £1,461,073, in 1931 the total is estimated not to exceed 400,000.

When we have a quantity that varies from place to place or from time to time, and we wish to obtain an idea of what the *Concise Oxford Dictionary* calls 'the generally prevailing degree or amount', we calculate an average. The form in which it is usually calculated is known precisely as the *arithmetic mean*, although it is more often referred to in ordinary language as the average. It is the sum of the individual values divided by the number of individuals. There are other averages, but they need not concern us here.

The notion of an average carries with it, by implication, the notion of variation; for we do not average an invariable quantity: we do not ordinarily talk of the average length of a day. When we calculate an average, however, we choose to ignore the variation and focus attention on the 'generally prevailing' value. This means a very big step in the process of statistical summarizing, substituting for the several individual values the one. Sometimes, however, people forget the variation they have ignored, and are misled by taking account of the average alone; and it is because of the prevalence of this error that statisticians are at great pains to stress the inadequacy of the average. It has its limitations, but provided they are recognized, there is no single statistical quantity more valuable than the average. When we read that the nation spent an average of 33s. a head a week on food in 1964 and calculate that the average expenditure on items of consumption was about £7. 10s. a head a week, we have two pieces of information that are striking and useful, even though they tell us nothing of the large variations from one person to another in the expenditure on food and in income. The average life of the 150 electric lamps mentioned in Table 5 (p. 35) is 1,452 hours, and if we use such lamps in the home, where we can let each one burn out before replacing it, that average means something. Such lamps at 2s. each are as valuable (as regards life) as lamps at 1s. each that have an average life of 726 hours; and this statement is true irrespective of the variation from lamp to lamp.

When a frequency distribution is, like that of the electric lamps, more or less symmetrical with a peak towards the centre of the range of variation, the average is an important descriptive constant, for it is near the typical value, and the variation is more or less the same above and below it.

Many quantities are in fact averages, although they do not always appear to be so. Thus, in the United Kingdom in 1965, there were 627,796 deaths in a population of 54,436,000, giving a death rate of 11.5 per 1,000. But the population is made up of people of all ages, following all sorts of occupations, and living in many localities, and for every sub-division of the population there is a separate death rate. The crude death rate is an average of all these.

Averaging is very useful in making index numbers. I have already described (p. 53) how, in order to measure changes in a quantity from time to time, the successive values are expressed as percentages of the value at some base period, to form index numbers. Sometimes, however, the quantity cannot be defined by a single measure, but is (mathematically at least) a somewhat vague and nebulous idea, like the 'price level'. The prices of the things we buy vary from time to time, but in different ways. Some prices rise and fall together, but to different degrees; some prices rise while others fall. For example, between 1920 and 1938 articles like motor-cars had a pronounced downward trend in price owing to changes in the methods of manufacture, whereas the price of coal did not change nearly as much. A good cotton crop may result in a low price for cotton in the same year that a poor harvest results in a rise in wheat prices. Behind all these various movements, however, economists see a movement in the general price level due to common factors that affect the prices of most, if not all, goods in somewhat the same way —factors such as war and money policy. One way of measuring this movement is to calculate index numbers for the separate commodities and then to average them in one way or another. The changes in the index numbers for any one commodity are due to the combined effects of the changes in the general level of prices and the special changes for the commodity; and in the process of averaging for many commodities the special effects tend to cancel out, leaving as the dominating factor in the combined index the changes in general level.

The index of retail prices is probably the best known of these indexes, being much used in public controversies on the cost of living and in determining wage changes. It has been in a state of development since the war and its basis has been changed. Currently (in 1967) the indexes for the different commodities are combined in such a way that they have the same relative effects on the average as recent expenditures on the corresponding commodities by consumers. These 'weights', as they are termed, are changed frequently in accordance with changes in the pattern of expenditure. Other important composite indexes measure changes in wholesale prices, industrial production, and prices of industrial shares.

Let us now consider the limitations of the average. Bowley has written: 'Of itself an arithmetical average is more likely to conceal than to disclose important facts; it is of the nature of an abbreviation, and is often an excuse for laziness.' The average does not measure the important facts that arise from the variation. In dealing with human problems such as nutrition, for example, it is as important to consider the individuals at the extremes as the average. It is no consolation to the families of classes C and D1 (Fig. 1) with four or more children, who can only spend a little over £1 a head a week on food, to know that the average national expenditure is 33s. a head a week.

We have seen that for the domestic consumer the average life of electric lamps has significance, but some large consumers such as public lighting authorities do not replace lamps as they burn out; they find it more economical to renew all lamps periodically, whether burnt out or not, and for them variability in life is important. Suppose such an authority decided that it would renew lamps at such intervals that only 4 per cent burn out before renewal (it would be very expensive to renew lamps so frequently that none were burnt out). Then for the lamps in Table 5 (p. 35), the renewals would be made after 600 hours of burning; for 6 lamps (=4 per cent of 150) have lives shorter than this. For this consumer the effective life of each lamp would thus be only 600 hours, and not the average life of 1,452 hours. Had the lamps been less variable, the effective life would have been nearer the average life.

Instances in which variation is of practical importance can be found in all fields—the strength of a chain is the strength of its weakest link, not that of the average link; owing to variations in the strength of his materials and in the load a structure will have to bear, the engineer designs the structure with a 'factor of safety'; the banker keeps a reserve of cash in the till to cope with variations in the demand for money; the authority that supplies water allows for variations from time to time in the rainfall when deciding on the capacity of its reservoirs; the electricity supply authority has to cater for a 'peak' load which, owing to variations in demand, is greater than the average load; and so on.

The average of a frequency distribution like that shown in Fig. 11 (p. 36) has the merit that it is near the typical value, but when the distribution is like Fig. 12 or 14, the average is not even typical. The average of the incomes of Fig. 12 is £850—rather more than the typical income of between £700 and £800 per annum. The average

age of the population of the United Kingdom (Fig. 14) was about 32½ years in 1931 and 36 years in 1961, but these figures are totally inadequate descriptions of the two distributions with their 'bulges'; and the information that the average age increased by about 3½ years between 1931 and 1961 does not disclose the differences discussed in connexion with Fig. 14.

Even for studying variations, however, the average can be of great use, for we can divide the whole field of investigation into sections and find separate averages for them. Table 1 (p. 18), for example, gives average death rates for the several age-groups, and shows the variation with age; the figures of food consumption represented in Figs. 1 and 2 (pp. 21, 22) are averages for the income groups, and show the variation in consumption with income.

Variation has an important effect on the average itself, if that average is a *weighted* one. The average death rate in the United Kingdom in 1965 was 11.5 a thousand, but this value is not obtained by adding up the twelve values given in the top part of Table 1 for twelve separate age-groups and dividing by twelve; such a calculation gives a rate of 33.1 a thousand. The rate of 11.5 results if, when combining the separate death rates, each is given a *weight* proportional to the number of people living in the age-group, and could be calculated arithmetically by multiplying the death rates by the corresponding numbers of people, adding the products, and dividing by the total number of people. The important point to notice is that such a weighted average depends not only on the quantities averaged, but also on the weights with which they are combined; and a change in weights may result in a change of average quite different from that which would result from a change in the quantities alone. I illustrate this from the following data.

The Registrar General divides Wales into two districts: Wales I containing the industrialized counties of the south, viz. Brecknockshire, Carmarthenshire, Glamorganshire, and Monmouthshire; and Wales II containing the remaining counties which are not as a whole so industrialized. The death rates for 1964 were 11.9 for Wales I and 13.2 for Wales II. In Table 12 I have separated the death rates according to age-groups sufficiently finely divided for present purposes, and we see that in each group, the rate is lower in Wales II than in Wales I except for the 5–35 age-groups—quite the opposite result from that of the crude total death rates. When we look at the age distributions of the populations in Table 12 we see the reason for this apparent discrepancy. Wales II contains relatively fewer of the younger men and women than Wales I and more people over 55. The death rate in Wales II is relatively high, not because that part of the Principality is more 'unhealthy' or dangerous to live in, but because it contains more aged folk who are relatively prone to die in any locality.

To obtain combined death rates not affected by this difference in age distribution, we must obtain weighted averages, using as weights the same population distribution for the

TABLE 12

Death Rates and Percentage Numbers Living at Various Ages

Age	Death Rate per 1,000 1964		Percentage Number Living mid 1963	
	Wales I	Wales II	Wales I	Wales II
0–1	27.2	21.5	1.7	1.6
1–5	0.9	0.8	6.6	6.2
5–15	0.3	0.3	15.1	14.5
15–35	0.8	0.9	26.2	25.2
35–55	4.4	4.2	27.1	25.7
55–65	17.3	15.6	12.0	12.8
65–75	43.9	40.3	7.6	8.9
75–	122.3	115.2	3.7	5.1
Total	...	...	100.0	100.0

two districts. Let us use the distribution of Wales I to give the weights. Then the weighted mean death rate for Wales II corrected to the age distribution of the population of Wales I is $(21.5 \times 1.7 + 0.8 \times 6.6 + 0.3 \times 15.1$, etc.$) \div 100 = 11.0$. This is substantially lower than the death rate of 11.9 for Wales I. This process of correcting a death rate to a standard age distribution is called *standardizing* the death rate. Commonly, death rates are standardized for the sex composition of the population as well as the age composition.

After the average of a series of figures, the next thing we usually consider is the amount of variation, ignoring for the time its form.

One measure is the *range*, which is the difference between the lowest and highest values in the series, and I use it later in this book because it is easy for the beginner to appreciate. It is not favoured by statisticians, however, except in limited circumstances, partly because it uses only the extreme values in the series and is unaffected by the spread of the values in between. The variation as a whole may be disclosed by measuring the individual values as differences from their average, and may be summarized by averaging these differences, thus obtaining a quantity known as the *mean deviation*. Another measure, called the *variance*, is obtained by squaring and averaging these differences, and the square root of the variance is the *standard deviation*. There are also other, less important measures of variation. The reason for having so many measures and for preferring one to another need not concern us here. It is sufficient to note that the measures are roughly equivalent—for example, they would all show a lower value for distribution (2) in Fig. 15B (p. 41) than for distribution (1).

Measures of variation suffer from the same general limitation as the average in that they ignore something—the form of the variation; but since it is not often that we need to compare distributions or series of data for which this form differs much, the limitation has less effect on the usefulness of the measures of degree of variation than on the usefulness of averages. Indeed, the averages and the measures of variation together cover most of the needs of the practical statistician, but their interpretation and use in combination require a good knowledge of statistical theory.

A development of great importance in applied statistics has taken place during the past few decades, and results from a recognition of the fact that variation is a composite quantity, resulting from the combined effects of a multitude of factors. The combined variation can be broken down into parts associated with groups of these factors and the relative importance of these groups as sources of variation thus be measured. This process, which belongs to a fairly advanced stage of statistics, is parallel to that of breaking down an average death rate, say, into sub-averages for several age-groups (Table 1, p. 18).

There are quantities for measuring the form of variation, and formulae including these have been devised for describing the general character of almost all the shapes of frequency distribution that are met with. It is perhaps a consequence of the uniformity of nature and a sign of the achievement of statisticians in condensing and summarizing data that with four constants, including the average and standard deviation, all the essential characteristics of most frequency distributions can be described; that these four constants can contain all the essential data from observations on hundreds of individuals. The measures of form of variation are difficult to interpret in practical work, however, and they are mostly of value in the development of the statistical theory on which practical statistical methods are based.

There are measures of association and correlation, but they require experience and a knowledge of statistical theory for their full appreciation. The most important is the *correlation coefficient* which measures the degree of correlation. If there is no correlation the coefficient is zero; and if there is a perfect correspondence such that changes in one character are exactly related to changes in another, the coefficient is plus or minus 1, the sign merely denoting whether the correlation is positive or negative. A value between 0 and plus or minus 1 describes a degree of correlation between these two extremes; the higher the value of the numeral in the coefficient, the greater is the degree of correlation. Measures of association and correlation are important in practical statistical analysis and with their aid conclusions can be reached from statistical data that would otherwise be missed. Another measure, the *regression coefficient*, describes by how much, on the average, one of the correlated quantities increases or decreases for a unit increase in the other—by how many millions of tons, for example, the wheat crop of Great Britain increases for each million of acres by which the area cultivated increases (Fig. 16A, p. 47).

Rates, ratios, and percentages; index numbers; averages, weighted and unweighted; measures of variation; measures of association and correlation; regression coefficients: these are among the most important tools of the statistician. Each of these describes some important feature of the data, each leaves much undescribed; each has its uses and its limitations. These quantities should be used carefully, as they are so easy to misuse, and it is perhaps advisable to leave their use mostly to the expert. But anyone may need to understand information expressed by them, and it is well that everyone should know at least something of their meaning.

6
Sampling

THE PRACTICE OF TAKING a small part of a large bulk or of an area of investigation to represent the whole is fairly generally understood and widely used. The housewife will 'sample' a piece of cheese at a shop before making a purchase; and a cotton spinner will buy a bale of cotton, having seen only a small sample of it.

One general reason for working with a sample rather than the bulk is that some appraisals of the thing in question involve destructive tests, and there is no point in appraising it if the whole is destroyed in the process: the housewife cannot eat her cheese and have it. The control of the quality of electric lamps involves estimating the life of batches of them; but the life of a lamp can only be measured by burning it to destruction and so samples are tested as a routine in manufacture. This kind of situation frequently arises in industry.

Samples are mostly used, however, because they are so much more economical to investigate than the whole bulk or field of inquiry. In controlling the quality of industrial products during manufacture, tests and measurements made on well-designed samples often characterize the whole of the output with sufficient precision for practical purposes, and inspection costs are then kept low by using samples as a routine, even where the test is not destructive. Sometimes it is technically better, as well as less expensive, to use a sample than to inspect every article in the output more cursorily.

Samples are much used in social and economic investigations. For example, it was recommended in 1954 that full British censuses of production and distribution should be taken at intervals of a few years, and that sample surveys should be made in between. In 1966 a miniature population census of one in ten households was made to provide information required for running the country. Some information is so difficult or costly to obtain that it is impracticable to deal with more than a sample. For example, it is important to know, for the purpose of constructing index numbers and for other purposes, how, on the average, various classes of household distribute their expenditure among such items as the various categories of food and clothing, fuel and light, holidays, hairdressing, and smoking; and surveys have been made to obtain the data. It is inconceivable that all households of any class in the country would or could keep accounts of the necessary accuracy and in the necessary detail; but when a sample is used a modest financial inducement can be offered to the participating households, and skilled investigators can be employed to help the housewives to keep accurate accounts following a standard pattern.

Sometimes a sample is used because of the speed with which the small quantity of data can be collected and dealt with. For example, interim results of the full British population censuses are now quickly derived from a sample of the returns. Samples can help in estimating various agricultural crops of a country before the harvest is complete and the full returns are available. One method is to estimate separately the area under the crop and the yield per acre. The area is usually known from full returns and the yield per acre can be estimated from early trial harvestings made on a sample of fields.

Altogether, the method of sampling is more than economical and convenient; it makes possible the gaining of knowledge that otherwise would never be gained. Its use has extended rapidly and widely during World War II and subsequently. Statisticians have enlarged their experience and have increased in the skill with which they handle the method, and users of statistics have increased the confidence with which they regard results derived from samples.

Samples do not, of course, give exactly the same results as the whole bulk or field of investigation; there are the so-called sampling errors, but they need not be so large as to render the results valueless. Some people unfamiliar with the use of samples are conscious only of the errors and entirely lack confidence in the results; they tend to dismiss the method as useless. Other people who use samples willy-nilly or by custom, ignore the errors entirely and take the results for more than they are worth. It is important for any user of statistics to avoid those extremes and to have a proper appreciation of sampling errors.

B. Seebohm Rowntree's 1941 social survey of York was made by visiting all households under investigation, but in his book *Poverty and Progress*, Rowntree also gave for comparison the results obtained from samples taken from the full returns. He made no comment on these comparisons (the differences are substantially what a statistician would expect), but a journalist commented on the figures as follows: 'Broadly speaking, they suggest that "sample-results" are usually within 15 per cent of the truth either way.' This statement is too broad to have a precise meaning, but in any event it is not the kind of generalization a statistician would make, for he knows that the error in a sample result depends on the size of the sample, on the nature of the bulk being sampled (particularly on the variation within it), and on the way in which the sample is taken. It is my purpose in this chapter to show how this comes about.

In the discussion I shall follow the usual practice of statisticians of referring to the bulk that is being sampled as the *population*. The population in this chapter is to be thought of specially as contrasting with the sample. I shall refer only to populations consisting of recognizably discrete individuals, e.g. men or electric lamps.

The ideal sample is the simple random one in which chance alone decides which of the individuals in the population are chosen. Suppose we wish to obtain a random sample of the people of England and Wales in order to make an estimate of their average height. To do this we may, in principle, take about fifty million exactly similar cards, one for each person, and write each person's national insurance number on the appropriate card (giving suitable numbers also to uninsured dependents). These cards may then be put in a large churn, thoroughly mixed, and (say) one thousand cards be drawn, somewhat in the way the names are drawn for a sweepstake. The thousand people whose numbers are on the cards are a random sample, and we can measure their heights, find the average, and so obtain a figure which is an estimate of the average height for the population.

To investigate the error in the average so estimated we could, again in principle, subsequently measure the heights of all individuals in the population and so obtain the true average. An easier thing to do is to draw a number of samples, each of one thousand, and calculate the several averages. These will vary above and below the true, or population value, and the extent to which they vary gives some idea of the error with which any one sample estimates the true average.

To do such an experiment in fact requires far greater resources than I can command, but there are other experiments that are similar in principle and are easier to do. What we really want to know is how chance works in deciding the choice of the sample; and chance also operates in games of the table, with such things as cards, dice, and roulette wheels. In these games, a population does not exist in the sense that the population of England and Wales does, but we may use the concept of a *hypothetical* population. Suppose, for example, we threw a perfectly balanced six-sided die millions of times. We should expect one-sixth of the throws to score aces, one-sixth to score twos, and so on; and the average score would be $\frac{1}{6}(1+2+3+4+5+6) = 3.5$. These millions of throws are a population, and any thousand of them including the first thousand is a random sample. But the millions of throws need not, in fact, be made; they need only be imagined as a hypothetical population, of which any number of actual throws form a sample.

To illustrate the way in which random sampling errors arise I have made an experiment which I need not describe in exact detail. The experiment is equivalent to that described here, which is not quite so easy to perform but easier to imagine. The imagined apparatus consists of ten packs, each of ten cards, the cards in each pack being numbered respectively 1, 2, 3, . . . 10. The packs are shuffled separately, one card is drawn from each, and the ten numbers on the cards are added to give a score. For example, the numbers might be 2, 4, 2, 10, 2, 5, 9, 2, 9, 8 and the score would then be 53. Then the cards are put back in their packs, the packs are reshuffled, and again ten cards are drawn to give another score. This is repeated, so that a large number of scores results, which are individuals from a hypothetical population consisting of the very large number of scores that could conceivably be obtained. The lowest conceivable score is 10, resulting from ten aces; the highest is 100, resulting from ten tens; and the true average score is 55. Now let us consider the results of the experiment.

It would take too much space to give in full the results of a really extensive experiment, but enough are given in Table 13 to show the kind of thing that happens. The top part of the table gives the first thirty individual scores. Chance has not given a score as high as 100 or as low as 10, as it might have done, and presumably would have done had I continued long enough with the experiment. The first thirty scores vary between 36 and 72, the range being 36. Now, in order to see what happens when we take samples and find the averages, I took 30 samples, each of ten scores. Such samples are far too small for most statistical inquiries (although statisticians sometimes have to be content with small samples) but they illustrate the errors of random sampling. The average scores are in the middle

TABLE 13

Individual Scores and Average Scores in Samples of Ten and Forty

				Individual Scores					
52	46	72	53	36	55	42	56	61	53
56	65	48	54	62	65	48	65	61	60
58	42	58	46	63	61	68	53	54	43

				Averages of Samples of Ten					
52.6	58.4	54.6	52.6	48.6	54.0	52.8	50.8	46.0	55.8
53.4	59.4	55.0	56.2	61.6	53.6	54.2	56.8	52.3	54.0
56.7	55.2	56.3	52.3	53.8	57.8	55.9	61.8	58.6	49.2

				Average of Samples of Forty					
54.6	51.6	53.6	56.6	54.3	55.1	57.3	54.4	56.0	55.4
55.3	54.1	55.8	55.4	56.0	53.2	55.1	54.3	54.8	54.2
54.3	57.2	53.2	56.0	54.5	51.5	53.7	56.0	54.8	55.4

section of Table 13. The first average of 52.6 is obtained from the ten individual scores in the top row of the table. The thirty averages vary between 46.0 and 61.8, the range being 15.8, and no average differs from the population value of 55 by more than 9.0. In so far as these thirty samples show the variations we are likely to get in the averages of the millions of samples we could draw, we may say that the biggest error with which the average of any one sample of ten scores estimates the population average is 9.0. When I took larger samples, each of forty scores, I obtained results given in the lowest section of Table 13. They vary between 51.5 and 57.3 with a range of 5.8, and the biggest error with which any one sample of forty scores estimates the population average is $55 - 51.5 = 3.5$. Thus we see that the averages estimated from random samples vary among themselves and differ from the average for the population, but that the biggest error decreases as the size of the sample is increased from ten to forty; and you may take on trust that this tendency would

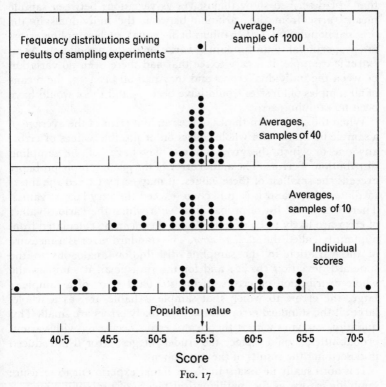

FIG. 17

have continued had I extended the experiment to deal with still larger samples. For example, by calculating the average of the thirty averages of samples of forty, we have the average of a single sample of 1,200 scores, which comes to 54.8—very close to the population value of 55.

These results are shown in the frequency distributions of Fig. 17 where, instead of a frequency for each sub-range, there are dots, each dot representing an individual score or the average of a sample. Notice how the averages tend to be clustered more closely round the population value as the size of the sample is increased. A frequency distribution of sample averages for any given size of sample is called the *sampling distribution* of the average.

The errors of random sampling, which in an experiment like that just described show themselves as variations between sample means, arise from the variation between the individuals in the original population. Other things being equal, such sampling errors are proportional to the amount of variation in the population. As an extreme example, it is easy to see that had there been no variation between the individual scores and they had all been 55, the means of all samples of all sizes would have been 55 and there would have been no sampling errors.

When the statistician thinks of the random error of the average of a sample he thinks of a whole collection of possible values of error, any one of which the given sample may have: of the sampling distribution of errors. The actual error of the given sample probably exceeds the smallest of these values; it may easily exceed the intermediate values; and it is unlikely to exceed the very largest values. There is a whole list of probabilities with which the various values of error are likely to be exceeded, and these can be calculated from a quantity called the *standard error*. The standard error is a measure of the variation in the sampling distribution analogous to the standard deviation (p. 62) and for the statistician it sums up the whole distribution of errors. If the standard error of a sample is large, the errors to which that sample is liable are, as a whole, large; if the standard error is small, the likely errors are small. This quantity, carrying with it the idea of errors occurring with various probabilities, should replace the cruder 'biggest error' I introduced in describing the results of the experiment.

It is not usually necessary to do an actual experiment to measure sampling errors, as the mathematical theory of probability enables statisticians to deduce sampling distributions and standard errors theoretically. This method is better because it is less laborious and more exact, giving results as accurate as an experiment involving millions of samples. The results of the theoretical calculations are of the same kind as those given by the experiment, and in some instances they have been checked by very large-scale experiments.

I have considered only the sampling errors of the average, but the same principles apply to other statistical quantities such as ratios, and the measures of variation and correlation. The theoretical deduction of sampling distributions of the many statistical quantities in use is a very highly developed branch of mathematical statistics; and sometimes the problems have proved so difficult to solve that statisticians have had to fall back upon actual sampling experiments. These are examples of what is sometimes termed the Monte Carlo Method, and are enormously facilitated by the use of electronic computers.

With the ability to calculate errors of sampling, statisticians can make allowances for them when making deductions from sample results. It is a standard procedure to examine the results of a sample to see how far they can be explained by random errors.

Before going on to the more practical problems of sampling, I will summarize the ground covered so far. When many samples of the same size are taken from a population of variable individuals, the sample averages show variation which may be described by a sampling distribution and measured by the standard error. A given sample of that size may have any one of the averages in the distribution, and the probability that its error will exceed any stated value can be calculated from the standard error. The standard error of the average is a measure of the errors to which a sample average is liable. For a sample of given size, this standard error increases as the variation between the individuals in the original population increases; for a given population, the standard error becomes smaller as the size of the sample is increased. (For the sake of the mathematically minded it may be stated that the standard error is inversely proportional to the square root of the number in the sample.) Consequently the random errors can be made as small as we please by making the sample large enough, and for a given population it is possible to calculate the size of sample necessary to reduce these errors to any desired value. Similar remarks apply to quantities other than the average.

The tendency for large samples from some population to have averages that vary little amongst themselves and differ but little from the population value is the reality behind the popular conception of the Law of Averages. This law does not operate, as some people think, so that an abnormally high individual score or run of scores is followed by an abnormally low score or run, correcting the average by compensation. In a random series, the scores following an abnormal score or run are quite unaffected by what has gone before; they tend to be nearer the general average than the abnormal scores are, i.e. to be more normal, so that when included in the average they reduce the effect of the abnormal scores. Averaging has more of a swamping than a compensating effect. Thus, if we may regard the days of weather as individuals from a population, the average weather for the population being the general type experienced at a given time of the year and place, the law of averages does not require that a very wet spell shall be followed by a very dry spell. For all I know, there may be a law to that effect, but if so, it is not the law of averages.

If the individuals in a statistical population are well mixed up, no known method of investigation can give more accurate results for a given cost than the method of purely random sampling just described, unless something is known about the individuals to enable some sort of selection to be made. Sometimes, however, a more complex form of random sample called the representative or stratified sample gives greater accuracy. Suppose, for example, that in a housing survey we wish to find the average number of rooms a family in some town. Some families at one end of the scale of wealth will live in one room each and at the other end there may be families that have say twelve rooms each; and this variation over a range of eleven rooms a family will give rise to a certain standard error in a simple random sample. Suppose further that we can divide the town into three districts—'poor', 'middle-class', and 'wealthy'—in each of which the total number of families is known, and that the range of variation of rooms a family is from one to seven in the poor, from four to ten in the middle class, and from six to twelve in the wealthy district. Then if we take a random sample from any one district, the district average is estimated with a smaller standard error than that just mentioned, resulting from a range of variation of six rooms a family (i.e. 7 minus 1, 10 minus 4, or 12 minus 6). Further, it can be proved that if a *representative* sample of the same size is taken, in which the proportion of families from each district is the same as in the whole town, the standard error of the average of that sample will be the same as the smaller error resulting from a range of variation of six rooms a family. This is because the proportion of families from each district is left to chance in the simple random sample; in the representative sample it is not, and that source of error is removed.

Random sampling is, however, the basis of the representative sample, which is nothing more than a weighted combination of random sub-samples.

Another form of sampling, superficially like representative sampling, is termed *quota sampling*; it is much used in social and market surveys. According to this method, after the number required in each stratum for the sample has been decided as it would be for a representative sample, those individuals are taken from the population according to the convenience of the sampler rather than according to some carefully operated randomizing procedure. Quota sampling is relatively inexpensive to operate and in skilled hands can give good results. But it is specially vulnerable to errors that cannot be calculated or controlled in the way that random errors can.

There are also other, more complicated, forms of sample, all aimed at securing the required information at minimum cost in different situations.

If it is granted that the ideal random sample can be a reliable instrument of investigation, the questions remain: Can the ideal be attained? Are the actual samples that are used as reliable as random samples? As a random sample is increased in size, it gives a result that progressively comes closer to the population value, whereas samples taken in some of the ways that are used give results that progressively come closer to some value other than the population value, results that may for some kinds of samples be too high, or for others too low. A sample of this kind is said to be *biased*, and the difference between the value given by a very large sample and the corresponding population value is called an *error of bias*. A biased die, for example, is one for which the fraction of throws showing an ace, say, tends to a value other than one-sixth (the value for the hypothetical population), and the greater the number of throws, the clearer is it that the fraction of actual aces is not one-sixth. Errors of bias are added to the random errors, and since they follow no laws from which they can be calcuiated, they must be specially investigated for each type of inquiry or, better, be eliminated entirely or reduced so that they become unimportant. The elimination of errors of bias may be difficult, and it is often necessary to use very elaborate sampling methods to achieve this.

It is nearly impossible for anyone to select individuals at random without some randomizing apparatus. If a teacher tries to select

a few children from a class, he will tend to choose too many clever
ones, or dull ones, or average ones; or if he tries to be random, he
may select too many clever and dull children and too few intermediate ones. In selecting a sample of houses 'at random', the
investigator will be very unlikely to select anything like the right
proportions of large and small ones, shabby and smart ones, new
and old ones, and so on. Bias almost inevitably will creep in and this
is why quota sampling is not approved by many statisticians. This
is illustrated by the results of large experiments conducted on several
thousands of school children in Lanarkshire in 1930 to measure the
effect of feeding them with milk, on their growth during the period
of the experiment—about six months. At each school the children
were divided into two comparable groups; one group received the
milk and the other did not, and the effect of the milk was to be
measured by comparing the growth rates of the two groups. The
results for a number of schools were combined. In an experiment of
this kind, the accuracy depends very much on the two groups or
samples of children being similar on the average before the feeding
with milk begins, i.e. on one being unbiased with respect to the
other. To secure this, the children were selected for the two groups
either by ballot or by a system based on the alphabetical order of the
names. Usually, these are both good ways of making unbiased
random samples of the two groups, but the whole thing was spoilt
by giving the teachers discretionary powers, where either method
gave an undue proportion of well-fed or ill-nourished children, 'to
substitute others to obtain a more level selection'. Presumably the
substitution was not done on the basis of the actual weights of the
children, but was left to the personal judgement of the teacher. The
result was that at the start of the experiment, the children in the
group that were later fed with milk were smaller than those in the
other group, the average difference being an amount that represented
three months of growth. It has been suggested that teachers tended,
perhaps subconsciously, to allow their natural sympathies to cause
them to put into the 'milk' group more of the children who looked
as though they needed nourishment. This bias did not ruin the
experiment, but unfortunately the interpretation of some of the
results was left somewhat a matter of conjecture instead of relative
certainty, and there was later a certain amount of controversy
about some of the interpretations. The substitutions of the children
could have been done without introducing bias had the actual

weights been made the basis, and there would have been an improvement on the purely random sampling; but by unwittingly introducing the bias, it seems that the teachers actually made matters worse.

A sampling method that is very liable to give biased results, particularly when testing opinion on controversial matters, is that of accepting voluntary returns. An undue proportion of people with strong views one way or the other are likely to make the returns, and people with moderate views are not so likely to take the trouble to represent them. For this reason, the post-bags of newspapers and Members of Parliament do not give random samples of public opinion.

A spectacular, and classical, example of a biased sample is provided by the attempt of the American magazine, the *Literary Digest*, to forecast the results of the Presidential election of 1936 by means of a 'straw vote'. Some ten millions of ballot postcards were sent to people whose names were in telephone directories and lists of motor-car owners, and several million cards were returned each recording a vote for one of the candidates. Of those votes, only 40.9 per cent were in favour of President Roosevelt, whereas a few weeks later in the actual election he actually polled 60.7 per cent of the votes. Those from among telephone users and motor-car owners who returned voting cards did not provide a random sample of American public opinion on this question.

Bias does not result only from obviously bad sampling methods; it may arise in more subtle ways when a perfectly satisfactory method is modified slightly, perhaps because practical conditions make this necessary. In some pre-war Ministry of Labour samples of the unemployed, a one per cent sample was made by marking every hundredth name in the register of claims, which was in alphabetical order. Bias was introduced by not confining the inquiry to the marked names; instead, the first claimant appearing at the exchange whose name was marked or was among the five names on either side of the marked one, was interviewed to provide the necessary data. Claimants who were in receipt of benefit attended at the exchange several days in a week, whereas those whose claims were disallowed but who were maintaining registration only attended once a week. The effect of this and of the latitude allowed in the choice of persons for interview was that too many claimants in receipt of benefit were included in the sample. It was only when the existence of this bias was realized that some of the results that were apparently inconsistent with other known facts made sense. A similar kind of effect can arise in surveys of households if no one is at home when the investigator first calls at some house chosen to be one of the sample. Such houses are likely to contain small families with few or no young children, since in large households someone is almost certain to be at home to answer the door; and unless the houses with no one at home are re-visited, the sample will be biased in respect of size and character of household.

Although there is no general theory of errors of bias by which the amount of such errors can be calculated in any particular instance, as can be done for random errors, statisticians do not work entirely in the dark. Sometimes the sample gives, as part of its results, information that is also known accurately from a full census, and the sample is usually regarded as free from bias in all respects if in this one respect it agrees with the census. The soundness of the results of a sample inquiry may sometimes be checked by comparing them with data obtained in other ways, perhaps by other investigators. Where none of these checks are available, it may be necessary to rely on the statistician's general experience of sampling methods in deciding whether the sample in question is a good one. I have given enough examples to show that a good deal is known of the ways in which errors of bias arise, and what must be done to avoid them.

It is implicit in my definition of errors of bias that they cannot be 'drowned' by taking very large samples, in the way that random errors can; a fact that the experience of the *Literary Digest*'s straw vote on the American Presidential election of 1936 amply confirms. From this point of view, a good sample can be arrived at only by employing a good sampling method. I have already mentioned some methods incidentally, and it is only necessary here to give it as a warning that when a statistician advises adherence to an elaborate method with a closeness that may seem to the layman to be 'fussy', that advice had better be followed; failure to do so has been known to lead to biased results.

The first task of the statistician in a sample inquiry is to design the method of sampling and the size of sample so that the results are precise enough for the purposes of the inquiry and the cost is reduced to a minimum. For this he will use general knowledge and experience, but he may also require the results of a pilot inquiry.

The second task is to assist the practical people to take sampling errors into account when making inferences from sample results, and systems have been elaborated for doing this. The oldest system is that known as *significance testing*. This arises most characteristically when two samples are taken from two populations in order to see whether the populations differ. For example, we may have two samples of men to discover if Englishmen differ from Scotsmen in average height. If the difference between the two sample means is so large compared with the sampling errors that it could not reasonably be attributed to the chance effects of those errors, it is said to be *statistically significant*. If the difference between the Englishmen and Scotsmen is not statistically significant, that does not imply that there is no difference in average height between the two populations; it merely implies that any difference is swamped by sampling errors. Historically, significance testing was developed first, but there is now a tendency to regard the above-mentioned first task of the statistician as the more important.

In industry, when samples are used to decide whether individual consignments of goods come up to specification the system of decision is closely related to that of significance testing. Suppose the goods are being tested for strength. A rule is often adopted that the consignment must be rejected if the average strength for the corresponding sample is below a certain value or accepted if it is above. Then, because of sampling errors, there is a risk that a consignment with a high average strength (i.e. a satisfactory consignment) may be rejected or a consignment with a low average strength (i.e. an unsatisfactory consignment) be accepted. Either event is unfortunate from some point of view. The person who is presenting the goods wants them to be accepted; he must be willing to run some risk of rejection but if that risk is to be small he must present goods with a substantially higher average strength than the specified strength. For a given specified strength and level of risk this higher average strength can be calculated from sampling theory. This is the average strength to which the goods must be produced if undue rejection is to be avoided—let us term it the 'produced' strength. The unfortunate event for the other party to the transaction—usually termed the consumer—is the wrongful acceptance of a consignment of low average strength. If the consumer can regard as satisfactory a consignment with a strength lower than the specification level, the risk of wrongful acceptance can be low, and for a given risk this lower strength can also be calculated from sampling theory—let us term it the 'utilized' strength. Of the many consignments assessed by the testing procedure, those with an average strength above the 'produced' strength are unlikely to be rejected, those with a strength below the 'utilized' strength are unlikely to be accepted, those with an intermediate strength will have a very uncertain fate. Although some, perhaps many or even most, accepted consignments will have average strengths above the 'utilized' strength, the consumer will be unsafe to count on this—he will regard every consignment as having the 'utilized' strength and no more.

There is an economic aspect to the problem of sampling in industry. It usually costs money to increase strength so that the difference between the 'produced' and 'utilized' strength represents a cost which can be reduced by narrowing the gap between the two strengths, and this in turn can be achieved by increasing the size of the sample and hence by increasing the cost of testing. There is an optimum size of sample which will reduce the sum of the two costs to a minimum, and the statistical theory of sampling is an important element in the determination of that optimum.

I have discussed a simple but typical situation in order to illustrate the issues that arise in the use of samples to assess the quality of industrial products. Actual situations are often more complicated. If a consignment fails at the first test a second sample may be taken; and this kind of procedure can be extended. Sometimes use can be made of the information that the consignment is from a producer who normally produces satisfactory goods; and sometimes the testing scheme is designed to secure, not that individual consignments are up to specification, but that a long run of consignments is satisfactory on the average. In all these situations, however, the same basic sampling theory is used in determining the economic and technical consequences of any proposed sampling scheme and in determining schemes to meet the practical requirements.

Altogether, the method of inquiry by sample is difficult and full of pitfalls. But statisticians could not get on without it and experience of its use is both wide and deep, so that in competent hands the method is capable of giving results that are reasonably accurate. Moreover, the inevitable errors in the results can be estimated, and allowance can be made for them in arriving at conclusions.

7

Taking Account of Chance

CHANCE OPERATES in many fields besides that of random sampling, and many of its effects can be calculated by applying the same general methods as are used to calculate the errors of random sampling. Some of the further applications of those methods will be described in the present chapter.

The effects of chance can be calculated only because they follow certain laws, but these differ in kind from the *exact* laws of subjects like physics. Events that follow exact laws can be described or predicted precisely; but we can only specify probabilities that chance events will occur, or specify limits within which chance variations will probably lie. Newton's laws of motion, for example, are exact because they describe exactly the relations between the motion of bodies and the forces acting upon them; the errors of random sampling follow chance laws because we cannot predict exactly what average a random sample will have; we can only state, as I have suggested on p. 70, the probability that it will lie within certain limits. The word 'stochastic' is used as an adjective to describe the element of chance.

I cannot embark upon a full discussion of what we mean by chance, but as a preliminary I shall indicate a few ideas associated with the word. Statisticians attribute to chance, phenomena (events or variations) that are not exactly determined, or do not follow patterns described by known exact laws, or are not the effects of known causes. That is to say, the domain of chance varies with our state of knowledge—or rather of ignorance. Such ignorance may be fundamental because the relevant exact laws or causes are unknowable; it may be non-essential or temporary, and exist because the exact laws do not happen to have been discovered; or the ignorance may be deliberately assumed because the known exact laws and causes are not of such a character that they can profitably be used in the particular inquiry in hand.

An example of ignorance that, according to present-day ideas, is fundamental, is in the Principle of Indeterminacy of modern physics; we do not and cannot know the precise motion of an electron. We do not know what determines the position of a shot on a target, but that ignorance is non-essential and in some degree temporary. The variations in the positions of the shots depend on a host of factors such as variations in the primary aim of the marksman, the steadiness of his hand, the weight, size, and shape of the bullets, the propelling charges, the force of the wind, and so on; but presumably these factors can be investigated and laws be discovered. Indeed, this has happened; and the history of gunnery shows the temporary character of the ignorance. Gunnery is much more of a science and more exact than it was in the days of the Battle of Waterloo, or even during the 1914–18 War; and as knowledge has increased, unpredictable variations in placing of shots have been reduced; but at each stage these variations are regarded as due to chance. (Missiles that seek out the target are excluded from this discussion.) Ignorance of causes is assumed by an insurance company in using its past experience of accident claims to establish future premiums for motor-car insurance. The company has considerable knowledge of the circumstances surrounding every past accident on which a claim is made, but is unable to make more than limited use of that knowledge, and so treats the accidents against which it insures largely as chance events, except for a few special allowances such as 'no claims bonuses' or extra premiums charged to people with bad accident records.

Usually, events regarded as coming within the domain of chance are those governed by a complicated system of many causes, each of which produces only a small variation; and one frequent characteristic of such events is that small changes in the circumstances surrounding them make a big difference to the results, just as, for example, a puff of wind may determine whether a drop of rain falling on the Pennine watershed will emerge into the North Sea or the Irish Sea.

Chance as I have described it operates in a very wide field, covering the whole of the unknown; but mathematical calculations can be made and chance laws be propounded only for comparatively simple systems covering a portion of this field. Nevertheless, such calculations have a wide range of usefulness, which the following examples will illustrate.

One use of chance calculations is for deciding which of the fluctuations in a time series are random and which are trends or special features having some significance. By way of example, consider the changes in the numbers of deaths in the United Kingdom at ages up to 65 years, depicted by one of the lines in Fig. 10 (p. 31). The general downward trend up to about 1954 is apparent and may reasonably be attributed largely to the fundamental and slow-acting causes of improved health and medical services and better social conditions. This trend may be represented by a downward-sloping straight line which may be determined mathematically; such is an exact law or description.

Readers will have no difficulty in imagining such a line drawn through the zig-zag line in Fig. 10 for the ages up to 65 years and the period up to 1954. The actual deaths year by year differ from the numbers represented by the line, some above and some below, and the deviations may be regarded as being due to a complex of causes, including the weather. From a full analysis of the numbers of deaths due to the various causes and a knowledge of the events of each year it may be possible to explain the deviations, but we cannot bring such knowledge into a system and so assume ignorance. We consider the deviations as forming a chance system and apply to them the same laws as describe the results of games of chance and sampling experiments. This is the argument for applying the theory of errors of random sampling to testing the statistical significance of fluctuations in time series. For example, there is a fairly steady upward trend in the deaths at all ages in Fig. 10, with deviations. Application of the theory would show whether the low value in 1948 or the peak in 1951 is part of this system, or whether it is an exceptional feature.

This kind of application of the theory, to the extent that it succeeds, enables us to decide in retrospect whether any particular events with which we try to associate fluctuations have had important effects compared with the system of random fluctuations. When following changes week by week or month by month as they occur it is useful, too, to be able to decide whether the last increase or decrease is large enough to call for action, or whether it is random.

At one period, for example, a local newspaper used to publish weekly figures of deaths due to road accidents in a certain town, and the number used to fluctuate about an average of four or five per week. But we should not worry if between two particular weeks the number rises from three to six, or rejoice if it falls from five to two. Such changes are no greater than any that can be attributed to chance, and do not indicate a real change in conditions. Sometimes the chance coincidence of random fluctuations may give rise to several small increases or decreases, giving a spurious appearance of a trend. Sampling theory can show when such is the case. At holiday week-ends, the numbers of casualties in road accidents are publicized daily and comparisons with previous years are commented upon. As a means of focusing attention on an important problem at a time when such attention can be effective, the exercise is useful. But statistical appraisal is necessary to make it useful as a means of advancing knowledge.

Many time series are more complicated than that used to illustrate the above argument. The trend may be represented by a curve rather than by a straight line, there may be superimposed a cyclical movement as in Fig. 9, or a seasonal movement as in Fig. 7. Analysis involves representing these features by some exact law, mathematically determined, and separating out the random and the exceptional fluctuations. Additional complications occur if the system of random fluctuations changes from time to time. For example, the periodic and random fluctuations in deaths due to measles in Fig. 6 decreased markedly over time, and a mathematical representation of the system would be very complicated. In more recent developments of the methods of analysis, the chance fluctuation is not regarded as producing a deviation from the slow movement for (say) one year and then ceasing to have effect, but as also influencing the values for subsequent years. For example, a high number of deaths in one year reduces the number of people available to die in subsequent years and so tends slightly to reduce the deaths in those years; this effect is added to the general trend and to the chance fluctuations in subsequent years. The methods for analysing time series have developed considerably since World War II and are now based on ideas that are sufficiently close to reality to give useful results.

The theory of random errors was used for measuring the accuracy of astronomical measurements long before it was applied to statistical samples, and it is used in measuring the errors of experimental observations in general. When the astronomer measures, say, the position of a star, he finds that in spite of the precision of his apparatus and the care with which he adjusts it and makes his observations, he does not get the same answer from successive determinations. He repudiates the idea that the position is varying and attributes the variations in his results to unavoidable errors of observation. The question arises: What is the true position? And if it cannot be measured exactly, how accurately can it be estimated? A similar situation arises in the other so-called exact sciences, notably in physics and chemistry. Several determinations have been made of the velocity of light, but they do not agree exactly; and a chemist would be very surprised if he got exactly the same result every time he measured an atomic weight.

This interpretation of experimental results as being due to an invariable quantity plus observational or experimental errors is purely a mental conception. The only reality is the set of observations, the characteristics of which can, if desired, be expressed by any statistical constants such as the average, or a measure of variation, or by a frequency distribution. For most experiments, however, it is useful and (within limits) valid to adopt the more common conception.

The errors do not follow any known exact laws, and so the laws of chance are sometimes used to describe them. In applying these laws, the results are regarded as a random sample from a hypothetical population of results, the average of this population being the true value. Then, the average of the sample is an estimate of the true value, and the error in that estimate can be calculated as for any statistical sample. Is this idea valid? On the face of things, it seems as reasonable to imagine the millions of results that would have been obtained had the experiment been repeated millions of times under the same conditions as to imagine the results of millions of tosses of a die. But it is not certain that the variations between experimental results are entirely of the same kind as those we get when we toss dice.

On this question there are differences of opinion among experimentalists. Some refuse to admit any similarities between experimental and random errors. Others, faced with otherwise intractable results, use the theory of random errors as the only way out. Experimental errors are not, in general, random. There are 'personal' factors, and any one person shows a bias that changes from time to time. I prefer to regard a set of experimental results as a biased sample from a population, the extent of the bias varying from one kind of experiment and method of observation to another, from one experimenter to another, and, for any one experimenter, from time to time. If this view is accepted, experimental errors can be regarded as forming a chance system, but the system is not as simple as that assumed in calculating the errors of random sampling.

In general the bias cannot be estimated and the theory of random errors is therefore not enough. Sometimes, however, one can say that the bias is likely to be small compared with the random errors, and then the theory may give useful, if approximate, results. For example, if, say, five separate chemists were to determine the atomic weight of an element independently, in different times and places, and possibly by different methods, the results would vary because of the effects of random errors and bias. But the separate biases for the five chemists would differ and so would appear as random errors between the averages for the five chemists, the group as a whole would probably exhibit but little bias, and the theory of errors would provide a reasonably close measure of the precision with which the average of the five chemist-averages estimates the true atomic weight. This might not be so, on the other hand, for the average of, say, twenty consecutive determinations made by one chemist in one laboratory.

Errors of bias are often relatively unimportant when the observed quantity is the difference between two similar quantities. In measuring the distance between two lines in a spectrum, for example, the main error is often due to the uncertainty of setting the cross-hairs of the measuring microscope on the centres of the lines. If there is a bias in doing this, it is likely to be similar for the two lines (provided they are not too dissimilar in width and appearance), and the difference in the two settings will probably be practically unbiased. The theory of errors gave a result that was at least qualitatively right, when applied to Lord Rayleigh's measurements of the density of nitrogen. He made a number of determinations on 'atmospheric' and 'chemical' nitrogen and found a difference in the two averages. Subsequent treatment by the theory of errors has shown that the difference is greater than can be attributed to random variations, and this result is in accordance with a real difference we now know to exist, owing to the presence of the rarer inert gases in 'atmospheric' nitrogen.

Where the bias is completely unknown, I doubt if it is possible to do more than hope that the true value lies somewhere between the highest and lowest of the actual values, and regard the average as an estimate of the true value, that is as good as, but no better than, any other single estimate that could be made from the data. It is, of course, the experimenter's job to reduce bias and random errors to a minimum.

To sum up, the theory of random errors may be usefully applied to some experimental observations, particularly of differences in values, but great caution must be observed on account of bias. Certainly such an application is no substitute for careful experimental control.

Much experimental work, particularly in biological subjects, is now done under conditions, many of which can be well controlled, and the observations can be made accurately; but the material is inherently variable and the results have to be treated statistically. The Lanarkshire experiment made to measure the effect of milk on the growth of children, already mentioned on p. 74, is of this kind. The amount of milk fed can be controlled, children fed and not fed with milk can be kept in the same environment, and the changes in weight can be measured accurately; but it would not do to base conclusions on an experiment on, say, two children. Children vary, and it is necessary to observe a large number and take averages.

The problem of interpreting the results of such experiments is essentially statistical, and it has fallen to the lot of statisticians to study the general questions of arranging experiments with variable material, of drawing conclusions from the results, and of testing them. Under the leadership of the late Sir Ronald Fisher, who started this work at the Rothamsted Experimental Station (for agriculture), an elaborate technique for doing this has been developed and is very widely used in almost all fields of study, including technology, where experiments are done. I propose to give some description of this subject.

There are three main principles to be observed in designing such an experiment; they are replication, randomization, and economy in arrangement.

The necessity for replication has already been stated. The problem first arose chiefly in agricultural field trials made to measure such things as the effects of various fertilizers on wheat yield. It was early seen that different plots treated in the same way gave different yields. Hence, it was not sufficient to have two plots, say, to treat one with a fertilizer, to grow the crops and measure the yields, and to regard the difference as measuring the effect of the fertilizer. The experiment has to be replicated by treating several plots in each way and measuring the difference between the average yields.

Even differences in such averages can be affected by variations between plots, as we can see from the results of the sampling experiment described in the last chapter; and it is desirable to estimate the accuracy of the observed difference. The only known way of doing this is by the theory of random errors. It was found, however, that variations in plot fertility were not random. There was usually a fertility pattern, e.g. a gradient in fertility across the field. In order that the theory of sampling could be applied, an element of randomization was introduced artificially by using some such device as a ballot to decide which plots should receive the various experimental treatments. This is a 'trick of the trade' for making fertility variations into a comparatively simple chance system. A statistician might apply this principle to the above-mentioned experiment of feeding milk to school children by tossing a coin once for each child, giving that child milk if the result is 'heads', say, and no milk if the result is 'tails'.

The pattern in fertility differences between plots in a field was used to increase the accuracy of experimental comparisons. Adjacent plots tend to be more alike than those in different parts of the field, and by comparing the treatments on adjacent plots the random variations affecting the comparison were reduced, with an increase in accuracy. The other way of increasing accuracy is to increase the number of plots, and hence the expense of the experiments; the arrangement using adjacent plots is therefore more economical. In the same way, had it been possible in the Lanarkshire milk experiment to use identical twins, giving milk to one of each pair, far fewer children would have given the same accuracy as thousands chosen at random. This kind of arrangement can be made to satisfy the condition of randomness sufficiently for the application of the theory of random errors in an appropriate form.

The above are the elementary principles of the modern approach to the design of what I shall term *statistical-experimental* investigations. The whole subject has, however, become very complicated as several experimentally imposed variations of one kind have been included, and experimentally imposed variations of several kinds. Thus, experiments may be done with various quantities and combinations of several kinds of fertilizer on several varieties of wheat. Further complication arises when experiments are done on different farms and in different years, and it is necessary to consider to what extent results obtained on one group of farms in one year apply to other farms and other years.

In spite of the fact that sound methods are available, experimenters continue to work with variable material on non-statistical lines, and they get discordant results which they cannot fit into a system. Different workers sometimes get different results in the same subject, and controversies arise. When, in such circumstances, the experimenters turn to sound methods of statistical analysis, involving proper experimental arrangements, difficulties of these kinds tend to disappear. Then, experiments which were previously done on an inadequate scale are increased in size, often they are designed more economically than before, and the advancement of knowledge is made more orderly and certain. Experiences of these kinds drive home the lesson that statistical principles should be consulted when an investigation is being designed, as well as in the analysis of the results.

Statistical methods are often regarded as applying only to very large numbers of observations, but that is no longer true. It would be far too costly to replicate some experiments hundreds and thousands of times, and statisticians have had to make do with small numbers. They have, however, developed the theory of errors to apply to small samples as well as to large ones, and it is usually this form of the theory that is applied in statistical-experimental investigations.

There are many chance events that occur in life to which the general theory of random errors may in some degree be applied.

For example, many telephone subscribers have access to one trunk line, and a multitude of causes determine how many will want to use it at any given instant, i.e. it is to some extent a question of chance whether more than one subscriber will want to use it at once and thus cause delay. In so far as this is true, the extent of delays of this kind can be calculated from the theory of probability which is the basis of the theory of errors. This is typical of a number of congestion problems that arise in telephony, in road and rail traffic, in the queuing of patients at a hospital, in the queuing of jobs for attention in a repair shop, in machines in a factory waiting their turn for attention from an operator, and so on; and although many of them are difficult mathematically, 'queuing theory', as it is termed, has been considerably elaborated and is providing practically useful results.

Accidents have a large element of chance in their causation—the

TABLE 14

Frequency Distribution of Men who had Various Numbers of Accidents. Comparison between Actual and Chance Distributions

(Data by E. M. Newbold, Report No. 34, Industrial Fatigue (later Health) Research Board)

Number of Accidents	Frequency of Men	
	Actual	Chance
0	42	5
1	44	21
2	30	40
3	30	50
4	25	48
5	11	37
6	12	23
7	15	13
8	8	6
9	8	3
10–14	19	1
15–21	3	...
Total	247	247

circumstances preceding a 'near shave' often differ by only a hairbreadth from those preceding a catastrophically fatal accident; and the theory of probability has been useful for studying accident problems in calculating the effects of chance and showing the importance of other factors. The following is an example.

Records were kept of the numbers of accidents that happened during the course of one year to 247 men workers engaged in moulding chocolate in a factory. Some of the men had no accident, some had one, some two, and so on, a few having as many as twenty-one accidents. The data are arranged in a frequency distribution in the first two columns of Table 14. Now we ask: Were all the variations between the men in the numbers of accidents they suffered due to chance, or were there differences between the men in their tendency to have accidents? Were the 42 men who had no accidents exceptionally skilful or just lucky; and were the 22 men who had ten accidents or more clumsy or unlucky? The average number of accidents per man is 3.94, and even if all the men were equally skilful in avoiding accidents, chance would give rise to some variation. It has been calculated from the extended theory of random sampling that this variation would result in the frequency distribution of the last column of figures of Table 14. This is very different from the actual distribution. We may say, roughly, that 5 of the 42 men with no accidents were lucky and the remaining 37 skilful; that one of the 22 men with ten or more accidents was unlucky and the remainder clumsy. Comparisons of this kind between actual and calculated chance distributions have led to investigations that have shown how people differ in 'accident proneness', i.e. in their tendency under given circumstances to suffer accidents. The chance distribution given in Table 14 is calculated by assuming a very simple system of chance variations; more complicated systems taking into account variations in accident proneness have been used in the more advanced investigations on the subject.

8
Statistical Laws

THE CENTRAL PROBLEM of statistics is dealing with groups variously described as collections, crowds, aggregates, masses, or populations, rather than with individual or discrete entities; with events that happen on the average or in the long run rather than with those that happen on particular occasions; with the general rather than with the particular. A fuller consideration of this aspect of statistics is the subject of the present chapter.

Again I shall use the language common in statistical writings and refer to *populations* of *individuals*. The population is regarded in Chapter 6 as something from which samples are taken, but here as an aggregate of individuals, which will in most instances be represented by a sample; I shall not here distinguish between the population and the sample.

The population has characteristics and properties of its own, which are essentially derived from and are an aggregate of those of the individuals, although the two sets of properties may be different in kind. In the population, the individuals merge and their individuality is dissolved, but from the dissolution rises a new entity like a phoenix from the flames. The population is at the same time less and more than the totality of the individuals.

This conception is not peculiar to statistics. Rousseau, for example, distinguishes in *The Social Contract* between the General Will and the wills of all the people:

In fact, each individual, as a man, may have a particular will contrary or dissimilar to the general will which he has as a citizen. His particular interest may speak to him quite differently from the common interest.

There is often a great deal of difference between the will of all and the general will; the latter considers only the common interest, while the former takes private interest into account, and is no more than a sum of particular wills: but take away from these same wills the pluses and minuses that cancel one another, and the general will remains as the sum of the differences.

The loss of individuality results from the method of the statistician in confining his attention to only a few characteristics of the individuals and grouping them into classes. Consider a married couple, say Mr. and Mrs. Tom Jones. As a couple their individuality consists in a unique combination of a multitude of characteristics. Mr. Jones is tall and thin, is aged 52 years, has brown hair turning grey, and is a farmer. Mrs. Jones is called Mary and at 38 years is still handsome; she is blonde and is really a little too 'flighty' for a farmer's wife. The couple have been married for 16 years and have three children: two boys aged 14½ and 11 years, and a girl aged 2. In addition to these and similar attributes the couple have a number of moral and spiritual qualities that we may or may not be able to put down on paper. It is by all these, and a host of other qualities, that their relatives and neighbours know Mr. and Mrs. Jones; the uniqueness of the combination of qualities is the individuality of the couple.

The statistician who is investigating, say, the ages of husbands and wives in England and Wales is interested only in the ages, and does not wish to describe even these accurately. So he puts our couple in that class (Table 8, p. 45) for which the age of the husband is 45–55 years and that of the wife is 35–45 years. Mr. and Mrs. Jones are now merely one of a group of some 320,000 other couples, and are indistinguishable from the others in their group.

Statistical investigations are not always confined to one or two characters of the individuals, and elaborate methods have been developed for dealing with many attributes, e.g. the ages of married couples at marriage, income, number of children, fertility of the grandparents of the children, and so on; but however many attributes are included, they are very few compared with the number that make up the individuality of each couple.

A population of individuals is the most characteristic and simplest chance system the statistician has to deal with. We do not know, or do not take any account of, the causes of the differences between the individuals, and so we dismiss them as being due to chance and fasten our attention on the population.

Statistics is essentially totalitarian because it is not concerned with individual values of even the few characters measured, but only with classes. However much we analyse the data to show the variation between the parts, we still deal with sub-groups and sub-averages; we never get back to the individuals. In studying the death rate of a country, for example, we may decompose the general average into sub-averages for the two sexes, for the separate age-groups, for different localities, industries, and social classes; but the death rate of an individual has no meaning. When we think of variation, we think of a mass of variable individuals rather than of one or two being very different from the remainder.

We have already noted in Chapter 3 that this part of statistical technique in selecting only a few characteristics for investigation, and in classifying the data, is not only necessary because of the limited power of the human brain to apprehend detail, but is a part of the general scientific method. It is an essential step in the development of general scientific laws. However much we know of Mr. and Mrs. Jones in particular, if we know nothing more we have no basis for drawing conclusions about married couples in general. It is only by paying attention to such features as individuals have in common with others that we can generalize. Individuals are important, as such, to themselves, to their neighbours and relations, and to professional consultants—the parson, the doctor, and the lawyer; they have no importance for the statistician, nor indeed for any scientist, except that they, with a host of other individuals, provide data.

Our first and, for most of us, our only reactions to our environment are individualistic. We *are* individuals, our experience is mostly with individuals, and even when considering a group we are conscious mostly of our personal relationship to it. The concept of the population as an entity does not come easily, and our ordinary education does little to correct this defect. The mental effort required to realize this concept is perhaps something like that necessary to appreciate a fugue with its contrapuntal pattern, as compared with the ease to a person brought up on hymns of following a tune with simple harmonies.

The characteristics of the population are described by frequencies and by the statistical constants and averages already described, but it is apparently so difficult to think of the reality behind these constants—the mass of individuals—that we personify the population and speak in such terms as 'the average man'. This is only possible because of a similarity between some of the measures of a population and those of an individual: the average height of a group of men is expressed in feet and inches, just as the height of one man is; but the similarity is only superficial.

We have already seen the inadequacy of the average as a description of variable material (Chapter 5), but the average individual sometimes is also a rather absurd figure. For example his age in the United Kingdom in 1931 was 32.5, and in 1961 it was 36 years; i.e. in 30 years the average man aged by only three and a half years! The average family can have fractions of a person. Books on the upbringing of babies usually contain a curve showing the growth in weight of an average baby; but few actual curves are like that. The curve for a real baby may be above or below that for the average and it may have a different slope in various parts. It will also usually have 'kinks' due to teething troubles and minor illnesses, whereas the curve for the average baby is fairly smooth; this paragon among children has no troubles!

Variation, as described on p. 37, is an important characteristic of a population that no individual can have. I have already been at pains to describe this in Chapter 5, and to point out how, for example, the deviations from any relationship shown by a contingency or correlation table are as characteristic of the data as the relationship itself. Indeed, without variation, a collection of individuals is scarcely a population in the statistical sense. A thousand exactly similar steel bearing balls (if such were possible) would be no more than one ball multiplied one thousand times. It is the quality of variation that makes it difficult at first to carry in mind a population in its complexity.

All the special properties of populations I have considered arise in aggregates of independent individuals, but there are additional characteristics due to interactions between individuals. The behaviour of men in the mass is often different from their behaviour as individuals. Some men affect (or 'infect') others, and such phenomena as mass enthusiasms and panics arise. We speak of mass-psychology. Similarly the effect of an infectious disease on a community of people in close contact is different from its effect on a number of more or less isolated individuals. Statistical description can take account of interactions between individuals.

Although the individuals in a population vary amongst themselves, the population itself is very stable. Sir Arthur Eddington has well said: 'Human life is proverbially uncertain; few things are more

certain than the solvency of a life-insurance company.' This means
that we do not know when any individual will die, but an insurance
company can estimate the incidence of death in its population of
policy-holders with great accuracy.

This contrast between individualistic variability and statistical
stability, and the fact that the latter emerges from the former, this
apparent paradox of order coming out of chaos, has from time to
time given rise to metaphysical speculations. People in the eighteenth
century, accustomed to considering the variations between individuals, seem to have been struck by the statistical regularities and
saw evidences of a divine order. Sir Arthur Eddington, on the other
hand, presumably taking for granted the regularity of the laws of
physics, was more struck by the compatibility with these laws of the
unpredictable variation in the behaviour of individual electrons, and
offered comfort to those who want to believe in free will and scientific
law at the same time. The practical statistician may accept it as a
fact requiring no special metaphysical explanation, that mass
regularities can often be discerned where the individuals apparently
follow no regular laws.

Galton writes of the regularity of form of the frequency distribution in the following terms:

I know of scarcely anything so apt to impress the imagination as the
wonderful form of cosmic order expressed by the 'Law of Frequency of
Error'. The law would have been personified by the Greeks and deified, if
they had known of it. It reigns with serenity and in complete self-effacement
amidst the wildest confusion. The huger the mob, and the greater the
apparent anarchy, the more perfect is its sway. It is the supreme law of Un-
reason. Whenever a large sample of chaotic elements are taken in hand and
marshalled in the order of their magnitude, an unsuspected and most
beautiful form of regularity proves to have been latent all along.

Let us re-examine the data from the sampling experiment
described in Chapter 6 and see if we can repeat Galton's experience
and recapture something of his mood.

I have extended the experiment to obtain 4,000 scores altogether.
The first thirty are given in the top part of Table 13 (p. 68) in the
order in which they occurred, and these together with the 3,970
other scores are the 'large sample of chaotic elements'—and chaotic
they undoubtedly appear. I then proceeded to marshal the scores
in the order of their magnitude by forming a frequency distribution,
and stage by stage stopped to look at the result as the distribution

began to grow. The results for 50, 200, 1,000, and 4,000 scores are in Fig. 18. Since the scores are whole numbers, I have not grouped them into sub-ranges; the scales of the distributions in the vertical direction have been reduced as the numbers of scores have increased.

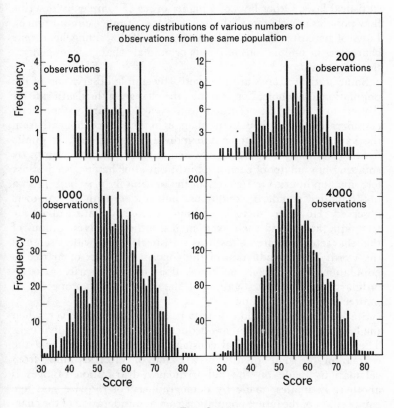

Fig. 18

At 50 scores, there is no sign of any regularity or form in the distribution, but at 200 scores, a vague suggestion of a form seems to be emerging; the scores show a slight tendency to pile up in the middle of the range. At 1,000 scores, the form is clearly apparent, although irregularities are still pronounced; but at 4,000 scores, the 'most beautiful form of regularity' is there, almost in perfection. It is not difficult to imagine the regularity that would be apparent were the sample so large as to be indistinguishable from the population.

The formulae and laws that describe populations and their behaviour as opposed to individuals are termed *statistical laws*. The various statistical constants mentioned in Chapter 5 are elementary statistical laws. Other laws of a higher order of complexity describe how populations change with time or place, or other circumstances. Laws of heredity, for example, are a way of describing how some characters in populations of plants or animals change from generation to generation.

Some statistical laws are discovered by simple observation of the population as a whole. For example, the change in the death rate for the country may be recorded from year to year, without any consideration being given to the changes in the chances of death from the various causes to which the individual is exposed. A public lighting authority could compare two batches of electric lamps by counting how many of each are burnt out after having been in use for, say, 500 hours. Or a colony of the banana fly may be kept in a bottle under standard conditions, and the growth in numbers observed. However, there is nothing necessarily statistical in the technique applied in such experiments, although investigations of this character are often classed as statistical in the widest sense of the word. The introduction of the concept of pieces of matter as populations of electrons or atoms does not necessarily turn an ordinary physical investigation of the macroscopic properties of matter into a statistical one.

Statistical methods and calculations are involved, however, when the laws for the population are deduced from those for individuals. The calculation of statistical constants is a case in point, and the estimation of some quality of a batch of electric lamps from calculations made on the full frequency distribution of lives is another. Estimates, made by demographers, of the size and age composition of the future population from a consideration of the characteristics of the present population and the various birth and death rates, are an important example of the statistical deduction of statistical laws. Such calculations may involve complicated mathematics.

It is implicit in all I have written that statistical laws have nothing to do with individuals. It is no exception to the statistical law that old men have old wives, on the average, if one old man of one's acquaintance has a young wife. A failure to recognize the distinction between the two types of laws sometimes leads to attempts to apply statistical laws to individuals, with paradoxical results.

We now return to the starting-point of this chapter—a consideration of individuals. They in the aggregate are the population, and from their characteristics we can calculate those of the population. We cannot perform the reverse process. Individuality is lost, as far as the statistician is concerned, for good and all. But this does not mean that we know absolutely nothing of the individual when we know the population.

Consider a single electric lamp taken at random from the batch represented by the distribution of Table 5 (p. 35). Even if we do not know its life, we know that it will be an exceptional lamp if its life is greater than, say, 2,800 hours—it will be one of 4/150ths of the batch. Indeed, it is more likely to be one of the 89/150ths of the lamps with lives between, say, 1,000 and 2,000 hours.

We are used, in ordinary life, to dealing with data of this kind by introducing the concept of probability. In the example quoted we would say that the probability of any one lamp having a life greater than 2,800 hours is 4/150 = 0.027, and that the probability of the life being between 1,000 and 2,000 hours is 89/150 = 0.593.

This is an application of what is commonly regarded as the statistician's definition of probability as a ratio of frequencies. Corresponding to any frequency distribution there can be calculated a whole series of probabilities of a random individual lying within various stated limits, and statistical probability is a device (a verbal trick!) for attaching to the random individual the characteristics of the whole distribution. In this way, a population is epitomized in an individual much more satisfactorily than in the concept of 'the average man'. But statistical probability does more than this. It corresponds closely to the more popular idea of probability as a measure of the strength of belief in a thing. Most people if asked what is the probability of a tossed penny falling heads uppermost would reflect that heads was as likely as tails and would reply: one-half. The statistician, if in a pedantic mood, would reply: in the hypothetical population of tosses, one-half of the total give heads, therefore the probability of a head is one-half. An alternative method of expression is to state that the chances of a head are even, or for the lamps, that they are 593 to 407 in favour of a life of between 1,000 and 2,000 hours.

Probability is, in ordinary life, also applied to events that do not occur as frequencies. We speak of the probability of or the chances in favour of a particular horse winning a race. Even in such instances, however, I think that people carry at the backs of their minds the idea of frequencies; they in effect imagine a lot of races, in a given proportion of which the particular horse wins. The idea is described in the following quotation from a lecture given by Karl Pearson in 1892:

A friend is leaving us, say in Chancery Lane at 4 o'clock in the afternoon, and we tell him that he will find a Hansom cab at the Fleet Street corner. There is no hesitation in our assertion. We speak with knowledge, because an invariable experience has shown us Hansom cabs at 4 o'clock in Fleet Street. But given the like conditions within reach of a suburban cab-stand, and our statement becomes less definite. We hesitate to say absolutely that there will be a cab: 'You are sure to find a cab', 'I believe there will be a cab on the stand', 'There is likely to be a cab on the stand', 'There will possibly be a cab on the stand', 'There might *perhaps* be a cab', 'I don't expect there will be a cab', 'It's very improbable', 'You are sure not to find a cab', etc., etc. In each and every case we go through some rough kind of statistics, *once* we remember to have seen the stand without a cab; on occasions few and far between, 'perhaps on an average once a month', 'perhaps once a week', 'every other day', 'more often than not there has been no cab there'. Certainty in the case of Fleet Street passes through every phase of belief to disbelief in the case of the suburban cab-stand. If once a month is the very maximum of times I have seen an empty cab-stand, my belief that my friend will find a cab there today is far stronger than if I have seen it vacant once a week. A measure of my belief in the occurrence of some event in the future is thus based upon my statistical experience of its occurrence or failure in the past.

Thus probability in its most general use is a measure of our degree of confidence that a thing will happen. If the probability is 1.0, we know the thing will certainly happen, and if the probability is high, say 0.9, we feel that the event is likely to happen. A probability of 0.5 denotes that the event is as likely to happen as not, and one of zero means that it certainly will not. This interpretation, applied to statistical probabilities calculated from frequencies, is the only way of expressing what we know of the individual from our knowledge of the population.

Statistical laws, which describe the characters and behaviour of populations in one way or another, may be transformed into probabilities—i.e. from them the probabilities and frequencies in the population may be calculated. Thus, statistical laws are the chance laws referred to in the early part of Chapter 7.

It may have been noticed that probabilities have been calculated from the frequencies of a distribution, either known as for the lamps, or assumed as for the penny. In general, it is necessary to have some data on which to calculate probabilities. I have been asked what is the probability of some queer or interesting event, without having been given any data. Statisticians do not evolve probabilities out of their inner consciousness, they merely calculate them.

The foregoing presents the statistician's view of probability, which is very widely accepted. Some scientists, including statisticians, also adopt a wider view, applying the idea to situations of uncertainty where a frequency of events cannot be envisaged, and deriving rules for making inferences in such situations.

9
Statistical Reasoning

STATISTICAL FACTS may have interest purely as a description of something that has happened or of an existing state of things, and certainly have great value in practical affairs. But we are seldom content with this use; we try to interpret the facts and expect them to tell us something of the underlying processes at work in the world we are studying. It is in this connexion that statistics is mostly misused. In this chapter I propose first to illustrate some of the misuses, and then to describe the ideas behind the ways in which statisticians try to learn from statistics. Statistical reasoning is not really different from any other kind of reasoning, and since the statistical method is a special case of the general scientific method I shall devote some attention to the latter.

I think that there are two reasons why statistics are so much misused. First, the desire to interpret them is so strong within us that it is almost an instinct, and we are apt to embark on interpretations too easily, without adequate mental preparation, and even without training in scientific habits of thought. Consequently we tend to jump to the superficially obvious conclusions, which all too often are not the correct ones. The interpretation of statistics is a matter for the expert—although one may be an expert without necessarily having a university degree in the subject. Secondly, statistics are so often made to serve the purpose of a propagandist—the man who does not use figures to arrive at the truth of a matter, but thinks he knows the truth and only wishes to convince other people. The propagandist may misuse statistics honestly, from ignorance, or dishonestly and deliberately; or he may countenance that more

subtle form of dishonesty of presenting data in a way that is formally correct, but misleading, leaving it to the public to draw the obvious but false conclusion. This last trick is most insidious when it is accompanied by some remark intended to disarm criticism, such as: 'I know these figures may be interpreted in several ways, but . . . .'

One favourite trick of the propagandist is to use some impressive but irrelevant figures to give a spurious appearance of precision under the cover of which a dubious argument is 'slipped across' to the public. Commercial advertisements sometimes do this. 'Five thousand and sixty-seven typists were asked what they prefer in shoes and four thousand nine hundred and ninety-five, or 98.6 per cent, prefer comfort to smartness; therefore buy XYZ shoes.' That is the kind of argument one has met.

A common source of error is the use of inaccurate data, of misleading methods of presentation, or of data that are so incomplete as to be misleading. I have shown in Chapters 2 and 6 many ways in which this may arise. Here is an example about a subject that was during the war of a very lively concern to the British public. On 13 May 1941 most newspapers reported the following facts of the numbers of German night bombers brought down in raids over Britain:

The total for the eleven nights of May now stands at 133; the previous highest figure was 90 for the whole of April.

That suggests an enormous improvement in the effectiveness of British night defences. Indeed, the quantitative impression is of an increase in the number of bombers brought down per night from $90/30 = 3.0$ to $133/11 = 12.1$. This comparison should not be so interpreted without a knowledge of the numbers of bombers used. Those figures were not given, but we noticed at the time that most of the raiding in April was confined to the ten or eleven nights before that of the full moon. Full moon was on 11/12 April and 10/11 May. Up to and including the night of 11 April, 51 night bombers were brought down, giving a rate of 4.6 per night. This is less than the rate for the first eleven nights of May, but not so much less as the figures originally quoted suggest. We cannot be sure that the number of nights before the full moon is the significant basis of comparison, but it is almost certain that the crude comparison gave an impression which, to the Britisher, was unduly optimistic.

The pattern of cause and effect in the world which produces

statistical data is very complicated, and to any set of figures several plausible interpretations are usually possible. It is a common error to consider or give only one interpretation, to the exclusion of others that may be equally reasonable but perhaps less agreeable to the propagandist. The following advertisement appeared in 1931:

It is men of exceptional experience who are buying X . . . cars today.

87 per cent of X . . . cars today are bought by men who have owned six other makes of cars before.

I suppose it is unlikely that as many as 87 per cent of all makes of cars are bought by such veterans as those mentioned in the advertisement, and the purchasers of X . . . cars are probably exceptional, but they may be exceptional in their fickleness—and do the makers of the X . . . cars wish us to believe that they do not get many repeat orders? Those are possible interpretations of the data. Alternatively, if X . . . cars were relatively expensive, most people would not be able to afford them until relatively late in their motoring careers. X . . . cars (which in 1967 are still on the market) may, for all I know, be as good as most other makes, and better than many; but as a recommendation, the facts of the advertisement are practically valueless.

The following extract from a letter to a newspaper breaks several rules of statistical good conduct:

An inquiry some years before the last war was made in certain towns all over England, Manchester included, as to the effects of the use of oatmeal among children and in public institutions, and the following is taken from it: in Manchester 2,333 children in all were questioned. In one school of 200, 84 per cent were regular users, and the teacher stated, judging from regularity of attendance, that those getting oatmeal were the most satisfactory.

In a girls' school of 182 pupils 33 had porridge, and the headmistress reported:

'The majority of oat-users are strong children, well nourished, and class work good. The non-users are not so strong and more liable to take colds and infectious diseases, and class work only moderately good.'

Other data of the same kind were given, all purporting to show the virtue of oatmeal. Now the essential information in the above extract is the better health of children who use oatmeal, but this is given only in vague qualitative terms. No statistician would rely on such general impressions as are quoted. What were the attendance results of the oatmeal-users as compared with the others? What were their sickness records? Moreover, the poorness of the data is covered over, doubtless unintentionally, by some very exact but irrelevant figures. It does not matter two hoots how many children were questioned, or how many took porridge. Without these figures, the data would be seen to be what they are—weak. However, even if the facts are taken at their face value, the letter-writer errs in considering only one of the factors that could have contributed to the alleged results. Most people take milk with porridge, which might be extra to milk taken otherwise, and that might be the cause of the improved health. All we know, if we know anything from the data, is that oatmeal plus milk plus the condiments are good for health, as compared with the food that is eaten as an alternative.

Wrong conclusions are sometimes drawn from data of quantities that change in time—we have already noted a change in the correlation of wheat crop with yield and area in Fig. 16 as compared with that in the corresponding figure in the 2nd edition of this book. It is a standard part of the statistician's functions to recognize 'nonsense correlations'. For instance, Udny Yule referred to the fact that the proportion of marriages solemnized in the Church of England and the death rate for the country had for many years been decreasing—there was a correlation between the two quantities. I doubt, however, if anyone supposes that this fact implied a causal relationship, and that a law prohibiting the solemnization of marriages in Anglican churches would reduce further the mortality rate of the nation.

A neglect to consider the errors of sampling or the effects of random fluctuations sometimes leads to false interpretations of statistical data. These effects have been dealt with in Chapters 6 and 7.

So much for the things that should not be done in handling statistical data. Let us now consider the more positive aspect of what should be done. To provide a special case, on which the discussion will be centred, I will remind the reader of Lamb's Dissertation upon Roast Pig'. According to Lamb's imaginary Chinese manuscript the art of roasting, or rather broiling, was accidentally discovered in the following manner. A swineherd, Ho-ti, left his cottage in the care of his eldest son Bo-bo, who, being fond of playing with fire, let some sparks escape into a bundle of straw, and the fire reduced the cottage to ashes.

Together with the cottage . . . what was of much more importance, a fine litter of new-farrowed pigs, no less than nine in number, perished. Bo-bo was in utmost consternation. . . . While he was thinking what he should say to his father an odour assailed his nostrils. A premonitory moistening at the same time overflowed his nether lip. He stooped down to feel if there were any signs of life in the pig. He burnt his fingers, and to cool them he applied them in his booby fashion to his mouth. Some of the crumbs of the scorched skin had come away with his fingers and for the first time in his life (in the world's life indeed, for before him no man had known it) he tasted— *crackling*! . . . The truth at length broke into his slow understanding, that it was the pig that smelt so, and the pig that tasted so delicious.

When Ho-ti returned there were at first the misunderstandings Bo-bo expected and feared, but gradually the great truth was borne in upon Ho-ti's mind and ultimately 'both father and son fairly sat down to the mess, and never left off till they had dispatched all that remained of the litter'.

Ho-ti of course wanted more roast pig, and so, 'as often as the sow farrowed, so sure was the house of Ho-ti to be in a blaze'; and later, after the secret had been dragged into the light in a law court, 'there was nothing to be seen but fires in every direction'.

This is an example of the empirical method. Certain results are observed to follow from a certain set of circumstances, so in order to repeat the result the circumstances are repeated. This method is often regarded disparagingly, but it is widely and successfully used. If we know that certain desired ends can be achieved by certain means, we rightly use those means, without waiting until we can find out how they work and if all the means are necessary to achieve the ends. Our forefathers would have been foolish had they waited for the discovery of vitamin C before making use of the knowledge that fresh vegetables in the diet prevent scurvy. Indeed, medicine is a fine example of the successful use of empirical knowledge (I do not imply that medicine does not also use scientific knowledge).

The empirical method, however, does not take us very far, and often leads us astray. Experience leads us to believe that always, if we can re-establish exactly all the circumstances that gave rise to a result, that result will be repeated exactly; but we can never be sure of re-establishing all the circumstances. Moreover, not all of them are essential, and without some analysis of the causes that operate we may repeat certain non-essential circumstances and omit essential ones. For example, we are not told which way the wind was blowing when Ho-ti's house first burnt; as it happened that did not matter, but if it had mattered, and Ho-ti had not taken it into account, the empirical method might have failed him. He was lucky to have included the important factor in his subsequent trials.

The empirical method is not only uncertain; it is often wasteful. Not only was it wasteful for the compatriots of Ho-ti to burn their houses in order to roast pigs, but the failure to discover the general science of the use of heat for cooking may have involved them in burning their boats to cook fish and might even have led to disastrous experiments into the burning of crops to improve their taste. It is desirable to discover the causes of an observed phenomenon so that the essential factors can be reproduced in the most advantageous way and applied generally.

Finally, it is only when our knowledge of the causes is fairly detailed that we can continue with investigations to improve the result. Until they had discovered that it was the application of heat that cooked the pig, it would scarcely be feasible for the people of Ho-ti's time to experiment with the effects of different degrees of heat and discover the uses of boiling, frying, and so on.

All the foregoing are utilitarian reasons why we are not content with the empirical method, but transcending them all is the intellectual desire we have to 'explain' things; to describe the relations between different happenings; to reduce our knowledge of the universe to as few general principles as possible.

It is the main function of science to analyse the causes of events and build up a system of general laws, and so we regard scientific knowledge as the opposite of empirical knowledge. This is the sense in which I use the word scientific in this book. Science and empiricism, however, differ only in degree, and scientists of the present generation, at least, are very modest in not claiming any sort of finality for the laws they formulate. Ho-ti was working on the very lowest level of empiricism when he burnt his house to roast pig and he would have been more scientific had he recognized that it was only necessary to have some sort of fire. We know now that even fire is not necessary, and that heat of a sufficient degree produced in any way, e.g. electrically, will roast the pig; but it is conceivable that some scientist of the future will discover the essential chemical and physical changes that occur when pork is roasted and will give us other ways of achieving the result. What the next stage after that can be I cannot imagine, but it would be very rash to say there will be no next stage. The point is that none of these stages is purely empirical and none is purely scientific; they differ only in degree.

The scientific method is so efficient, and has been successful in giving man so much power over his environment—power to construct as well as to destroy—that we are apt to overlook its limitations. A scientific description is by its nature a simplified description of a phenomenon and its relation to other parts of the universe, and is far from complete. This has been shown strikingly in connexion with the science of dietetics. Earlier in this century, food values were largely measured in terms of calories and the chemical constituents—fats, carbohydrates, proteins, and so on. Then it was found that these things were not enough, and that a diet was deficient unless it contained a due quantity of the various vitamins. It is because they have no faith in the completeness of the existing scientific description of dietetics that most people prefer to rely mostly on the empirical method in arranging their diet, choosing to eat such natural foods as general experience has shown to be good, and relying on special sources of vitamins only in special circumstances.

I think that considerations of this sort may lie at the root of the so-called mistrust of logic and reason that is sometimes attributed to the English. To mistrust logic and reason is—well, *irrational*; but it is not irrational to lack faith in the completeness of the data on which some reasonable conclusions are based. Such an argument does in some measure justify the Englishman's alleged preference for empiricism or 'muddling through' and for his reluctance to follow general principles to their 'logical conclusion'. It is certainly important in statistical investigations not to forget that the data do not tell everything, and that in their summarized, reduced form they leave out a lot of information that may be important.

Let us imagine how a physicist, working in our modern spirit, but with the knowledge available at the time of Ho-ti, would investigate the phenomenon of the production of roast pig, to discover which of the circumstances surrounding Bo-bo's and Ho-ti's experience were essential. He would first consider, as far as he was able, all the circumstances: the fact that there was fire, that the fire started in straw, that a house was destroyed, that there was a wind blowing in some direction (unrecorded), that the pigs were new-farrowed, and so on. Then, if he was painstaking but unimaginative, the physicist might conduct a series of experiments, reproducing in each one of

STATISTICAL REASONING 107

the circumstances in some way different from Bo-bo's. He might put the pig in or over a log fire; kindle the fire in the house with paper instead of straw; destroy the house over a litter of pigs by gunpowder instead of fire; and so on. In this way, he would soon discover the irrelevance of everything but fire and pig, although he might be a bit puzzled because all fires did not produce the desired effect (if they were not hot enough or did not last long enough, or were too hot or lasted too long). This last observation would probably lead him to try cooking the pigs on fires of various sizes and durations —and so the process would go on.

This is the experimental method of investigation: the method of producing the circumstances surrounding a phenomenon in various ways and combinations, but always under experimental control. The art of this method lies in the proper choice of combinations of circumstances and in the craftsmanship of exercising the required control; and if these have been well done there is little difficulty in correctly appraising the results, although great acumen may be necessary to weld them into a coherent scientific theory.

In most fields that are the subject of statistical inquiry, the opportunities for controlled experiments are very few. Society will not permit many experiments on man. So the statistician, debarred from varying the circumstances surrounding the subject of his investigation, has to observe the results of such variations as occur without his intervention and learn from them, disentangling as much as he can from the 'tangled skein' of causes and effects. Thus, if the Chinese authorities had prohibited experiments by the physicist into the production of roast pig, the statistician would be called upon to observe closely the results of the fires that appeared 'in every direction', in the hope that the circumstances surrounding them would be varied enough to enable him to decide which were essential and which were not.

This limitation does not preclude the application of scientific methods, as some scientists suppose. How much experimenting can the astronomer and meteorologist do? Are they unscientific? Surely it does not matter, in principle, whether the variations in circumstances that are studied are produced by the investigator, or not. The important thing is that sound reasoning should be applied to the interpretation of the results.

The method of inferring laws from observations on systems that result from uncontrolled variations is to many people *the* statistical method. Indeed, Udny Yule has defined statistical methods as 'methods specially adapted to the elucidation of quantitative data affected by a multiplicity of causes'.

There are three main ways in which the statistician treats observations so as to separate the effects of the various causes. Sometimes (unfortunately not very often) he can observe two things that differ to an important degree only in respect of the one factor under investigation; and then a straightforward presentation of the results tells us everything about its effect. The second way is to correct for the effects of disturbing factors, just as we corrected for the difference in age composition when comparing the death rates of the two districts of Wales (p. 60). The third way is to eliminate by averaging the effects of disturbing factors that operate in various directions. For example, if we wish to measure the effect of town as compared with country conditions on the death rate, we might first measure the rates for a number of towns, correct for age and sex distribution, and then average the results, expecting that the variations between towns due to other factors such as climate and locality will average out. Then we might do the same for a number of country areas. The difference between the two averages would then be regarded as measuring the effects of interest.

The use of correlation methods is an extension of this idea. As I have already stated, the trend shown in Fig. 16A (p. 47) discovers the average effect on the wheat crop of changes in the area cultivated, and the diagram is arranged to emphasize this effect. A correlation may result directly from the operation of a cause, but I have already emphasized that its existence does not prove a causal relationship. A careful analysis is necessary before such an interpretation of a correlation is legitimate, and usually there must be additional grounds to support it. In this analysis, statistical methods play a part, particularly the method known as *partial correlation*. The following is an example.

In an investigation by Professor D. V. Glass into factors associated with changes in birth rates, the following data for 1930–2 for the separate counties of England and Wales were used: (1) the gross reproduction rate, which is similar to the net reproduction rate (p. 53) except that no account is taken of the incidence of death; (2) the percentage of females over 15 years of age who were unmarried, which I shall call the percentage spinsterhood; and (3) the percentage of females over 15 years of age who were in employment, which I shall shortly describe as the employment rate. These three quantities were taken in pairs and correlated (see Chapter 4 and p. 47), with the following results: (*a*) there was a correlation coefficient of −0.433 between factors (1) and (2), expressing a fairly weak but definite tendency for the reproduction rate to decrease as the percentage spinsterhood increases—a result not unexpected; (*b*) the correlation coefficient between factors (1) and (3) was −0.625, expressing a stronger tendency for the reproduction rate to decrease as the employment rate among women increases; (*c*) there was a correlation coefficient of +0.530 between factors (2) and (3); i.e. the greater the percentage spinsterhood the greater is the employment rate among women. On the face of things, it looks as though a high percentage spinsterhood and a high employment rate both reduce the reproduction rate; but these two quantities are not independent, and their effects are intermingled. Suppose, for example, the employment rate of itself had no real effect on the reproduction rate; it would reflect in some degree the influence of the percentage spinsterhood and show an *apparent* effect on the argument:

high percentage spinsterhood leads to low reproduction rate,
high employment rate is associated with high percentage spinsterhood,
therefore, high employment rate is associated with low reproduction rate.

This effect could explain some, at least, of the apparent correlation between factors (1) and (3); and, similarly, any causal effect the employment rate had could explain some of the apparent correlation between factors (1) and (2). The method of partial correlation enables us to separate out these effects. The *partial correlation coefficient* between factors (1) and (2), which measures the effect of percentage spinsterhood alone, is −0.15, expressing a very weak association, which is of negligible importance. That is to say, if the employment rate among women is kept constant, the percentage spinsterhood is practically unrelated to the reproduction rate. The partial correlation coefficient between factors (1) and (3) is −0.52, so that if the percentage spinsterhood is kept constant there is an appreciable tendency for a high employment rate among women to produce a low reproduction rate. These results, as far as they go, suggest that, in order to increase births, it is not much good increasing marriages, but the discouragement of employment among women might have some effect. It is necessary in giving this summing up of the results to emphasize the words *as far as they go*. The results only apply to such variations as occurred between counties in 1930–2, and there may be other important causal factors, of which no account has been taken.

I have described the exhaustive investigation of all the circumstances surrounding the first production of roast pig as sound but unimaginative; progress in science has been much facilitated by the imaginative procedure of using working hypotheses in planning and making investigations. I cannot discuss this method of approach to a problem in full, but roughly it consists in making a tentative hypothesis based on existing knowledge and ideas, and testing it by arranging experiments that give one result if the hypothesis is correct, and another if one or more of a number of alternative hypotheses are correct. For example, the Chinese physicist, on being told that Bo-bo and Ho-ti both burnt their fingers when they first touched the pig, might, in a flash of genius, see that heat had something to do with the transformation of the pig, and would direct his experiments to testing the hypothesis that fire was the only factor of importance. As admissible alternative hypotheses, he might allow the possibility that the important factors were combinations of the nature of the combustible material, the direction of the wind, the age of the pigs, and so on. Then if he roasted pigs in two fires, in which the only common factors were fire and pig, and in which all the other factors differed, the physicist would at one blow test his hypothesis against the alternatives. If the pig was always roasted, his confidence in the hypothesis would be increased, although he could never be sure of it, because he could never be sure of having tested it against all possible alternatives. If the hypothesis was proved false he would have to think again, and, from his observations on the experiments already made, would form some new hypothesis which would in turn be tested. Used in this way, hypotheses are guides to experimental strategy.

In the early days of a new science there is little or no knowledge to form the basis of working hypotheses, and the patient collection of facts constitutes the main activity. Very soon, however, speculation on the meaning of the results begins, and tentative theories are developed. Then experiments and observations are made to test the theories, which are further developed, and modified or remade as a result of the new experience gained; and again the new theories are put to the test, and so on, experimental test alternating with theoretical speculation.

These two phases do not always proceed in the best order. I think, for example, that the early work of the biometricians (see p. 140) had biological significance chiefly in providing data, and that it failed to develop because it did not go far enough beyond this state. In economics, at least up to World War II, there has been an apparent tendency for theoretical speculation to outstrip verification by observation of the real world (p. 139).

The use of working hypotheses, both the main one and its alternatives (the alternatives are all too often neglected by the amateur), is very important in statistical research. They guide the statistician in planning his inquiry, in choosing what data to collect or use, in arranging and presenting them, and in deciding what statistical constants to calculate; and finally the results are examined in their light. Without such aid in selecting from the enormous range of possibilities, progress in knowledge would be slow, and much effort would be wasted in useless work. For example, in investigating the porridge question mentioned in the letter quoted on page 102 we might dismiss the likelihood of the condiments having any effect on health, and adopt the hypothesis that oatmeal and milk both have good effects, with the three alternatives that benefit is derived from (1) oatmeal alone, (2) milk alone, and (3) neither milk nor oatmeal. Then we would measure separately the health of children who took (a) oatmeal and milk, (b) oatmeal without milk, (c) milk alone, and (d) neither milk nor oatmeal; if it were impossible to find anyone who took oatmeal alone, an experiment might be necessary. If the question of the effect of the condiments was also included, the inquiry would be more complicated. In making these suggestions, I have neglected the important questions of the quantities of oatmeal and milk given to the children, and of the alternatives to these foods (for presumably children who do not eat porridge have something for breakfast); all these would need to be considered in a comprehensive study.

Thus, it is better to approach an inquiry in the light of existing knowledge, and to arrange it to answer certain specific questions, than to collect the data, subject them to a routine of statistical reduction, and then passively accept whatever results emerge. I do not deny that this passive approach may often yield good results, but it is inferior, except in some new field where there is no previous knowledge on which to base hypotheses. The use of statistical data to prove a case, in the sense of demonstrating it, is unscientific; but their use to prove a case in the old-fashioned sense of testing it is scientific and profitable. A statistical inquiry should be approached with a mind that is open but not empty.

The success of this method of approach depends to some degree on the main working hypothesis being somewhat near the truth. A false hypothesis can do no permanent harm, for ultimately it will be discredited, and investigations inspired by such often lead to valuable discoveries. Nevertheless, a false trail may for a time be set and time may be wasted; and an investigator who was too often on the wrong trail would not get very far.

There are no golden rules for the formulation of hypotheses, and their quality and success depend much on the knowledge and experience of the investigator in the field in which he is working, and on his intuition, acumen, and genius. Hypotheses may grow in the investigator's mind in the course of his work, they may come in a mental flash, or they may be suggested by some external accident. Some workers find it helpful to write individual facts on separate cards and play a kind of game of Patience with them, sorting the cards into combinations suggesting a variety of relations between the facts. The ability to formulate fruitful hypotheses and design experiments to test them is the quality of a first-rate scientist. In addition to this personal quality, habits of thought and even prejudice have their influence on the kinds of hypothesis that will be entertained. For this reason, impartiality is essential; and an investigator is most likely to be impartial if he is disinterested in the issue of the inquiry. The investigator should not be narrow-minded, and should be prepared to consider any reasonable alternatives to the main hypotheses he favours, but he cannot afford to waste his time on unreasonable ones. Sidney and Beatrice Webb, who have much of interest and value to say on the subject of social investigations, have written:

We have found it useful, in the early stages of an investigation, deliberately to 'make a collection' of all the hypotheses we could at that stage imagine which seemed to have any relevance whatever to the special kind of social institution that we were dealing with. We noted them all down on our several sheets of paper, and others as we went along; wise suggestions and crazy ones, plausible theories and fantastic ones, the dicta of learned philosophers and those of 'cranks' and monomaniacs, excluding those that we thought had no possible relevance to our work, such as the prophecies extracted from the measurements of the Great Pyramid, or those of the astrologers.

This passage suggests a breadth of outlook which I imagine most scientists would applaud, but not so many show; but even the Webbs stuck at taking astrology seriously. Yet I cannot see why they should exclude this and include the theories of cranks and monomaniacs; those who believe in astrology have a perfect right to say that, in this matter, the Webbs showed prejudice. The exact position at which one draws the line between what is reasonable and unreasonable is largely a personal matter.

Hypotheses formulated at any one time also tend to follow trends or fashions. For example there are great similarities between the theory of natural selection and the *laissez-faire* theories of economics, and there has been at times some vogue for applying the dialectical process to the pursuit of knowledge in various fields. The hypothesis used by the statistician in testing the statistical significance of results is that the observed variations and effects are due to random errors or chance rather than to the operation of newly-discovered causes, and he will hold to this as long as it is compatible with the data available. In this way it is an important function of the statistician to act as a devil's advocate against the admission of new knowledge. It has been said that 'Bacon was eminently the philosopher of *error prevented*, rather than of "progress facilitated".' The same may be said of the statistician in one of his functions and, although by improving and increasing the data available he also facilitates progress, he often appears to his scientific colleagues as a professional debunker of interesting conclusions. In the fields to which statistics is mostly applied the prevention of error is a most necessary function; there are plenty of people ready to facilitate progress.

Frequently, several reasonable hypotheses are compatible with the data, and then fresh data are necessary before any discrimination can be made between them. Even without such data, however, one hypothesis may be preferred to the others. The hypothesis already referred to, of chance being the cause of the effects, is a favourite one, and derives from the scientist's general preference for the simplest explanations involving the introduction of the fewest new quantities or ideas. Which of the possible hypotheses is the simplest depends on the investigator's idea of the general scheme of things, for the simplest is that which fits most easily into such a scheme. For example, some years ago data were given showing that the severity of attack from smallpox tends to increase as the time elapsing since vaccination increases, and is greatest in patients who have not been vaccinated. To those who are not against vaccination on other grounds, the obvious inference is that this treatment is effective as a protection against bad attacks of smallpox. Anti-vaccinationists, on the other hand, find it easier to explain the above data on theories which, to the outsider, seem very complicated. As a statistician I cannot condemn those theories, although as a man who generally favours orthodox views in science I prefer the more obvious inference.

Thus the statistical method, like scientific method in general, is based on certain fundamental principles, but it is not entirely automatic in its operation, and progress in knowledge depends to a considerable degree on the personal qualities of the investigator. He must be creative of ideas, yet should strike a nice balance between being too far-fetched and fanciful on the one hand, and being so conservative on the other that he impedes progress by his unwillingness to admit new knowledge and ideas.

I have insisted that the statistical method of investigation is scientific. Its critical apparatus is sufficiently well developed and discriminative to prevent an undue proportion of false conclusions being reached as a result of statistical inquiries (a certain amount of risk must be taken if progress is to be maintained). At the worst the verdict may be that a particular inquiry teaches nothing new. But the question remains: Is the method powerful? Do statistical investigations often lead to positive conclusions? In the next two chapters I give an estimate of the usefulness of the statistical method in the various fields of application, but here give only a brief general answer to the questions.

When clear conclusions emerge obviously from a simple arrangement of the data the statistical method is useful in a positive way. When, however, the pattern of causes and effects is complicated, and elaborate statistical analysis is necessary, positive conclusions are not often reached. So often, several hypotheses are compatible with the data, and when an analysis like the partial correlation of reproduction rate, spinsterhood, and employment, described on pages 108 to 110, is performed one cannot be sure that it is complete and that all factors have been accounted for. Consequently, the results of a purely statistical inquiry do not usually rise much above a fairly low level of empiricism, and any more scientific laws that are arrived at are largely justified on theoretical grounds.

The power and limitations of statistical investigation are well illustrated by the controversy of the 1950s and 1960s over cigarette smoking as a cause of lung cancer. A correlation between the degree of smoking and the risk of dying from lung cancer was established and generally accepted, but many people refused the obvious interpretation and offered alternative hypotheses. One plausible one was that some inborn characteristic in some people made them want to smoke and also made them prone to lung cancer. Additional information is required to test all the hypotheses and much research work, both statistical and in the laboratory, has been done. At present (in 1967) the weight of professional opinion favours the view that cigarette smoking is an important cause of lung cancer, but not all scientists are convinced. Statistical investigation has called attention to an important possibility and has helped in exploring that possibility in relation to others; it has provided a background and motivation for much valuable research; and it has helped to establish a strong body of responsible opinion on the causation of lung cancer; but it has been unable to establish that opinion beyond question.

I present this view of the limited powers of statistical investigation somewhat in a spirit of disillusionment. When first introduced to me, the methods of statistical analysis, particularly that of partial correlation, seemed to have unlimited power to penetrate the secrets of nature. I think, too, that this enthusiasm inspired the statisticians who developed the methods during the early years of this century and has been shared by many others, although I have no documentary evidence of this. Certainly, compared with such high hopes, the achievement has been disappointing.

Nevertheless I do not think that we should abandon statistical methods as useless. They *are* powerful, even if their power is limited, and there are fields in which only they can advance knowledge. We should persevere with them in a spirit that is steadfast, if somewhat chastened, believing that progress will be maintained, if more slowly and with greater difficulty than once seemed likely. Moreover, statistical methods are proving exceedingly powerful and are achieving much in the statistical-experimental kinds of investigations described in Chapter 7.

The use of statistics for discovering the forces at work in the social, economic, and similar spheres, where experiments are impossible, is a very difficult application of the scientific method. Many causes and effects are entangled so that it is hard to separate and relate them. Yet even the ordinary citizen needs to have some ability at least to distinguish what may be truth from what is probably falsehood, especially in a democracy where he has to make up his mind on many difficult public questions and contribute to the growth of public opinion. Surely it is an important task of education to give the citizen this ability by teaching the elements of statistical reasoning. If this is done, people will develop not only the ability to look at controversial social and similar problems scientifically and dispassionately, but also the habit of doing so.

10
Statistics in Affairs

THE USE OF STATISTICS in the business of running the country through its political, commercial, and social institutions—in those activities that determine the health, wealth, and happiness of mankind—is the oldest and the most considerable use. The Ancient Egyptians had a centralized form of government administered with the aid of systematic statistical knowledge of the economic conditions of the country (regular returns were made of the level of the Nile, on which the prosperity of the country so much depended). The English Domesday Book contains the results of a statistical survey, and there are evidences of statistics having been used in administration now and again during the subsequent centuries. Statistical information was used in a fairly elaborate way in the Italian states during the renaissance, to the extent that the historian Burckhardt declares that there was then produced 'for the first time a true science of statistics', the word 'science' in this context apparently connoting a practice of calculating the effects of various policies from data on populations and trade. There was in England a quickening of interest in commercial statistics early in the eighteenth century, but that only heralded a dawn which broke early in the nineteenth century. The importance of this aspect of statistical activity today is shown by the fact that most people seem to regard it as the whole content of statistics.

The need for statistical knowledge in running a concern increases as the concern becomes larger and more complicated. One man can conduct the affairs of a family or a small business with few figures, but as the scale of the enterprise becomes larger it becomes less possible for one man, or even a few men, to have at the same time the

necessary intimate knowledge of all the parts and the broad knowledge of the whole. Hence an organization is set up whereby the
men in central positions work largely through statistical knowledge
of the parts under their control—knowledge that is statistical in
the two senses of being numerical and summarized. As more
industries have fallen under the control of large combines, and more
of our activities have come under the control of the largest combine
of all, the State, statistical knowledge has become increasingly
important. Planning, in greater or less degree according to the government in power, is the order of the day, and without statistics planning
is inconceivable.

First let us see how statistics are used in running things after
policy has been decided. Their most elementary use in administration is in the balancing of the activities of one part of the system
against those of another to secure that supplies equal requirements
and that there are no 'bottle-necks' or parts not employed to the full.

For the national government, the necessary statistics range from
extensive figures of the expenditure of the various departments of
state, prognostications as to the course of trade for a year ahead, and
the yields of various taxes, required by the Chancellor of the
Exchequer in framing his budget, to the numbers of boots of various
sizes required to supply the army. Attempts are made to match
national programmes for building schools and recruiting teachers
to the expected number of children, and housing programmes to the
requirements of the population. War much increases the need for
figures of these kinds, and one has only to read economic and
administrative histories of the last war to realize how essential
statistics were to the direction of the war effort. In peace-time more
is left to the free play of economic forces, but even so the central
government continues to administer directly very large resources.

Local authorities need statistical information to enable them to
adjust their supplies of various public services to the needs, both
immediate and future, of the districts they serve. National building
and educational programmes are carried out by local authorities;
and when a new housing estate is being built, water, sewers, schools,
transport, and so on have to be provided, in quantities that are
sufficient but not excessive.

Statistics are also useful in public administration in providing
indications of how things are going and thus guiding action. A

classical statement of this function appears in the British White Paper on Employment Policy, presented to Parliament in 1944 by the Coalition Government. This paper, after accepting as a primary aim and responsibility 'the maintenance of a high and stable level of employment after the war', and indicating in a general way the economic and social policies that would have to be adopted and the methods that would have to be followed in attempting to achieve the aim, states the need for statistics in the following terms:

It is therefore vital for them [the Government] to obtain, more fully and much more quickly than they have in the past, exact quantitative information about current economic movements. Without this, informed control would be impossible and the central staff which it is proposed to set up would be left to grope and flounder in uncertainty.

The classes of statistics required are listed, and it is apparent that post-war developments in official statistics have been in part inspired by the ideas of the White Paper. Post-war developments have probably not been exactly those envisaged by the writers of the paper, but clearly the government's decisions on such items as import controls, monetary policy, taxation, and expenditure on capital goods such as schools and roads, have been much affected month by month and year by year by changes in such figures as the balance of payments, price levels, and the national income and outlay; and public appraisal of the government's actions has been informed by the same data. The policies of the successive post-war governments have differed, and for any one government have changed from time to time; but the administration of those policies and the assessment of their effects have been largely based on statistics.

The distinction between the formation of policy and its administration is not sharp, but we recognize that some decisions are fundamental and last for a relatively long time; these we call policy decisions. The scientifically-minded would wish, after the general aims have been decided, for all policies to be developed objectively on the basis of facts.

Since the war there has developed a subject called *operational research* which is largely a gathering together and development of subjects and methods already existing, but which aims explicitly at applying the scientific method to providing executive authorities in government and industry with objective bases and data to help them in arriving at decisions on policy. Statistics provides a good part of the content of operational research. However, the world of affairs is very complicated and the formulae of statisticians are too simple to fit it closely; and the data available are far from being complete and reliable enough for the purpose, especially as much of the necessary information involves forecasting what is going to happen in the future—an uncertain operation at best. Consequently, personal judgement and hunch necessarily enter very largely into the making of political decisions. Nevertheless, objective facts and scientific analysis, and in particular those associated with the subject of statistics, do play an important part.

Statistics can help by measuring some of the consequences of different policies; some of these consequences may rule out some of the policies, and thus the area for the exercise of personal judgement is reduced. For example, it may not be possible to determine objectively how much the country should spend each year on housing, but various estimates can be derived from such statistics as the numbers of houses in existence and the numbers of families. Comparisons can be made with corresponding pre-war figures and with figures for other countries, and the estimates can be related to the national income, the numbers of building operatives available, requirements for other forms of building, and so on. Data of these kinds provide pointers and thus the margin for the exercise of judgement and opinion can be limited.

Statistics can be useful, too, in calling attention to social and economic problems and in describing their nature. In the economic field: Which industries are expanding and which contracting? What changes are taking place in the localization of industry? Is there enough investment in capital equipment? In the social field: Does the level of infantile mortality vary with the district or with the wage of the father? Are deaths due to road accidents and to accidents in the home numerous enough to constitute social problems? What are the trends in crime of different kinds? All these are questions on which the light of statistics must be shed before political action can be considered. An example of the way in which statistics can disclose the nature of a problem is provided by a housing survey made in 1930 by the Merseyside Social Survey. The results showed that overcrowding was not due to poverty, since many a house was overcrowded even though it was occupied by more than one wage-earner earning good wages; a policy of subsidizing rents would not have been appropriate here. The recommendations of the so-called 'Robbins' *Report of the Committee on Higher Education*, issued by the British Government in 1963, for the expansion of the universities and on other matters were informed by a considerable body of statistical research.

Statistics giving indications of what is happening are useful in policy formation as well as administration. If things are wrong and going worse, some policy change is called for, although whether this should be in the direction of an intensification of existing policies or the adoption of new ones is not always clear.

Statistics guides policy-makers also in measuring the importance of various problems and placing them in a proper perspective. Although most economic and social problems are essentially statistical in that they concern masses or groups of people, towns, businesses, and industries, the men who have to deal with them are of the system, and since they have intimate contact with only a part it is not easy for them to see the whole. The views of the Member of Parliament are coloured by his knowledge of his constituency, which may be an agricultural or mining area; a business man tends to view all economic problems from the standpoint of his particular industry; the rent collector in a slum area sees overcrowding as the most urgent social problem; and the comfortable inhabitant of a prosperous town thinks there is nothing much wrong with the world. Some events strike our imaginations more vividly than others, either because of their nature or because of the publicity given to them. For example, a railway accident at Harrow in October 1952, in which 112 people were killed, created a great impression on the public mind. After that accident the British Railways announced that they were pressing ahead with the project of equipping, at a cost of several million pounds, main lines with automatic equipment that would prevent drivers of trains from passing signals set at danger—the cause of the Harrow disaster; and this action apparently met with general approval. But some people in private pointed out that between 1944 and 1953 deaths from rail accidents averaged only 65 a year and that only a small fraction of these were caused by drivers over-running signals; road accidents, on the other hand, averaged about 5,100 a year; and it was argued that from the point of view of saving lives it would be more effective to spend the money on the roads. The argument may or may not be valid and the decision of British Railways is not demonstrated to be wrong; but the statistical picture and the general impressions immediately following the Harrow disaster put the problems in a different perspective.

It is, however, a weakness as well as a strength of statistics that they paint a broad, impersonal picture; for some of the high-lights are lost. We have seen that statistical descriptions are essentially summaries that leave something out; and in connexion with social problems, in particular, that something is often the human touch which fires the imagination and spurs the will to action. Thus, had the Harrow accident been put into its statistical perspective in the public mind, no extra money might have been spent on accident prevention on either railways or roads. Moreover, the measure of human distress is not necessarily the number killed—the killing of one hundred people at one time and place may, according to some human values, be worse than the killing of many times that number at scattered times and places. Or again, statistics can show the prevalence of poverty but they cannot help the rich man to imagine what the life of the poor man is like. They can measure many of the conditions of life that promote happiness or misery, but they cannot measure happiness. The situation is well stated in the following passage from the periodical *Planning*:

Public opinion upon many social and economic problems still suffers from an incapacity to grasp statistics, and thus fails to measure either the size of each problem as a whole or the relative importance of its different aspects. In the case of unemployment and man-power, however, the reverse appears to be true; everyone is only too ready to think in broad quantitative terms, even at the price of forgetting that rows of classified statistics are no more than feeble symbols for a multitude of men and women, each of whom individually represents a special and unique problem, which cannot be satisfactorily treated while it is simply lumped into some immense aggregate.

The statistical description can be improved by analysing the 'immense aggregate' into sub-aggregates, as we have seen in the earlier chapters of this book, but at the best it remains only a partial description.

It is partly for this reason that the statistical investigator and the man who develops policy should not rely entirely on figures but should have direct contact with the problems with which he is dealing. The following passage by Bowley suggests a realistic approach to a social problem, with a good balance between the use of statistics, particular description, and direct contact:

If, for example, we know from the census account that in five per cent of the houses of a town there are more than two people to a room, if we ascertain that the worse houses are insanitary and small, and if we visit a few to find out the actual accommodation, the age and sex of the inhabitants and their occupations, we have probably all the data we need for criticizing or suggesting a policy of reform, without measuring the rooms or making a house to house visitation.

I have insisted at some length on the limitations of statistics, hoping to forestall the criticisms of those who doubt the value of the subject and to temper the enthusiasms of those who over-estimate its power, but even as a dynamic of economic and social reform exact statistical description has value. Beatrice Webb, showing the effect of the publication of the results of Charles Booth's 1886 social survey of London, stated: 'The authoritative demonstration . . . that as many as thirty per cent of the inhabitants of the richest as well as the largest city in the world lived actually at or beneath the level of bare subsistence—came as a shock to the governing class.' A more recent example concerns a bad fog (or 'smog') experienced in London in the winter of 1952, during which deaths due especially to respiratory causes increased spectacularly. This experience was widely and repeatedly referred to in the press, and even two years later a correspondent to a daily paper wrote: 'In addition, of course, we must never forget the 4,000 people who lost their lives in the last smog.' It is reasonable to suppose that the impression created by the statistical result added to the sense of urgency with which the problem of atmospheric pollution has been regarded. Generally, action taken as a result of an intellectual conviction derived from hard facts is likely to be more resolute than action stimulated by emotional appeal alone; and statistical facts are of the hardest metal.

In the affairs of business and industry statistics has broadly the same kinds of application as in public affairs. Many of the data concern costs; and the cost accountant, with his systems of handling and presenting financial data, provides guidance for business executives. Indeed accountancy has extended somewhat and there has grown up a whole subject and function termed *management accountancy*. As a consequence the functions of the accountant and statistician in business overlap—or it is better to think of the two professions as having a large ground of common interest. I shall discuss the help that statistics can give, recognizing that some of this help may be given through the medium of the accountant.

The big policy decisions for an industrial business are what to supply, how much to supply, and what price to charge. Goods that are ordered today, or for which manufacturing provision is made today, cannot reach the market for months or even years. In placing orders for a few months ahead, or organizing a factory for the next few months of production (for efficient factory production necessitates planning ahead), or building a new factory, these are the crucial decisions. Forecasts must be made of the likely costs of production under various conditions and of the future demand; and in siting a factory account must be taken of such factors as the availability of labour. As in other applications, the uncertainty of forecasts and the incompleteness of the information available leaves a large area for the application of judgement and subjective assessment, and even for guesswork; but statistics do provide considerable guidance. For example, a knowledge of the population in the market areas, its habits and wealth, and its age distribution, helps in the assessment of the probable size of the market for some goods; and a knowledge of trends in the general economic situation and the situation in particular sectors is also important. Business-men engaged in foreign trade are naturally concerned to know in detail and quantitatively what is happening internationally. Much market research also involves statistical surveys of consumers.

There are also policy decisions to be taken in industry which are more closely related to the technical side and in which statistical information and methods can go a long way towards defining the best course of action. For example, if a transport undertaking, covering, say, the whole country, provides a large number of small repair stations for its vehicles, the cost of transporting vehicles to the stations for repair is low but the costs of repair may be high. The provision of a few large repair stations may reduce repair costs at the expense of increasing transport costs; usually there is a number of stations for which total costs are at a minimum, and this number can, in principle at least, be determined from statistical data by statistical methods. In the running of a factory unavoidable irregularities in the delivery of raw materials and components, in the progress of manufacture, and in the demand for delivery of the products, require stocks of materials and partly manufactured goods to be kept at various stages. It is a statistical problem of some complexity to take account of these irregularities, of the loss due to the interruption of manufacture through stocks running out, and of the costs of maintaining stocks, and hence to determine the most economical size of stock. The even more technical problem of specifying manufacturing conditions and the qualities and dimensions of the products at various stages involves the problem of engineering specification in general, which has an important statistical side.

For business administration statistics are essential. For example the planning of production in a large factory or combine is now a part of what is known as *scientific management*, and many firms now have a planning department to co-ordinate the activities of the other departments. The requirements of the sales department with their delivery dates are translated into orders to the various production departments, with intermediate delivery dates so arranged that the final products are delivered as required; these orders are translated into orders for raw materials, tools, and labour, and the whole activity is organized and timed so that the work flows without interruption. Moreover, to secure efficiency, it is necessary as far as possible to balance the sizes of the various departments so that they are large enough to meet all demands made upon them and yet are not unnecessarily large. For this work, statistical returns and charts are much used. The whole subject is highly developed and involves special knowledge and experience, although the statistical methods used are not very elaborate.

Statistics also provides the measures of performance and efficiency that are required for the proper running of a large business. The higher executives cannot know in detail what is happening day by day in all the parts of a large concern and need summary figures to assure them that all is well and to indicate where action is called for; and even departmental managers and foremen are helped by having regular figures of performance. In the sales office, figures of sales are analysed and trends in time and differences between districts are observed and investigated. Well-elaborated systems of cost control give producing departments weekly or monthly records of the actual costs of production which may be compared with the 'standard' costs; and deviations give rise to investigation and action. There are a number of indexes of efficiency in use in industry. The railways assess operating efficiency by such ratios as the number of train-miles per engine-hour, and the efficiency of the administration of insurance companies is judged partly by the ratio of management expenses to premium income. In the factory, the output per man-hour or per machine-hour, the percentage of materials wasted or spoilt, or the output per unit of fuel consumption may be important. For coal-mining the tons of coal per man-shift are returned regularly in official statistics.

It is not to be supposed that such statistical indexes are so reliable that action can be automatic or apparently poor performance be condemned—a low value of the index may be due to conditions outside the control of the management and may indeed be accompanied by efficient management. The indexes merely show where it is profitable to make investigations. Since World War II statistical measures of labour productivity have been much used in industry. Both in the United Kingdom and the United States factories in the same industry have been compared; wide differences have been disclosed and the statistical results have guided activities aimed especially at improving factories at the low end of the productivity scale. International comparisons have been made, and although the results cannot be taken at their face value, they have stimulated considerable fruitful activity. Largely as a result of statistics showing the very much higher labour productivity in U.S. as compared with European industry, American methods of factory organization have, in post-war years, been studied and as a result European practices have been improved.

Statistical quality control is a well-developed subject concerned with providing industrial management with tools for controlling the quality of manufactured products in the routine of production, although its effects reach back to design. It operates in the same way as all statistical controls by providing higher management and customers with measures of the level of quality that is being maintained, and production management with indications on which action can be based. Statistics comes in partly because there is in the best of manufacture a certain amount of uncontrolled variation. For example, much of modern industry is run on the lines of mass production, and this involves making separately the standard parts of an article and then assembling them. If all the parts were exactly alike, they would fit together exactly, the finished articles would be exactly alike in character and quality, and all would be well. But this does not happen. The raw materials vary in quality, important processing conditions such as atmospheric humidity and temperature vary, tools and machines are used in various states of wear, and the operators, being human, cannot work with perfect precision. The consequence of all this is that the products vary. Some components differ in size or shape from the standard so much that they will not fit in the final assembly, some are too low in quality to give a satisfactory performance. Hence arise a number of questions: What variation in quality of raw materials shall be allowed before a complaint is made to the suppliers? Must every component be inspected or only a sample? And if a sample, how big should it be and how should it be taken? How much variation in quality may be regarded as normal and at what stage does an increase in variation suggest that something has gone wrong? What is the relative importance of different factors in causing variation? How shall variations in the products be allowed for in designing them?

All these questions require for their answer a mixture of technical and statistical knowledge. The role of statistics is the making of systematic records of quality, the development of measures of variation, the working out of the effects of changes in quality and variation, and the application of the theory of random sampling along lines already mentioned in Chapter 6 (p. 77).

Having dealt in a general way with the role of statistics in the development and administration of policy in practical affairs, I now consider some particular aspects.

Since many of the decisions of the man of affairs involve taking a view of what is going to happen in the future, considerable attention has been paid to economic and business forecasting as a branch of applied statistics.

The prediction of the future from a knowledge of what has happened in the past involves the belief that things will in some way continue to be as they have been. Sometimes we are naïve enough to think that the superficial appearance of things will continue to be—it is so easy to take the short view—but economic and business forecasting is based on a belief that the relations between past events have been determined by fundamental principles that are stable and will continue to be so. An empirical forecast based on a superficial analysis of past events cannot be very reliable, but the more successful we are in discovering the fundamental relations between events—the unchanging principles that govern change—the more scientific and reliable are our forecasts likely to be.

As an example, let us consider the prediction of the future population, which we do not expect to remain unaltered at its present level. To make a prediction we might plot a graph showing changes during the past few years, and might extend it forwards, continuing, say, the trend. In the absence of any reason for supposing that the trend will continue, that would provide an empirical forecast which might be roughly correct only for a year or two ahead.

Empirical forecasts have been given some cover of scientific respectability by assuming, on superficial theoretical grounds, that the population of any region develops in time according to some specific mathematical law. One such law describes the population as increasing slowly at first, then rapidly, and finally at a decreasing rate, until it levels off at a stationary, limiting size. Such a pattern of growth can be represented by a so-called 'logistic' equation, the constants of which can be determined if the actual population is known for a substantial early portion of the total development cycle. Then, the equation can be used to predict the population for the remainder of the cycle. When this method was applied to predicting the population of the U.S.A. from the actual figures for the years 1790 to 1910, the predicted value for 1950 was 148.7 millions, whereas the actual value was 150.7 millions. The close agreement was, however, fortuitous; and the weakness of the method is shown by the fact that an 'improved' prediction obtained from the actual figures for 1790 to 1940 gave 143.8 millions—the prediction for ten years ahead was not as good as that for thirty years ahead.

The fundamental approach to population-forecasting involves a consideration of the essential causes of population changes—births, deaths, and migration. If the appropriate rates for these can be predicted, the future population can be calculated exactly from the age-distribution of the present population; but that process merely shifts the problem of prediction. Demographers commonly make several calculations by making several plausible assumptions about the future of birth, death, and migration rates, and so obtain a range of possible future populations. For example, different predictions of the 1977 population of Great Britain made in 1947 for the Royal Commission on Population ranged between 46.9 and 52.8 millions. The *Annual Abstract of Statistics* for 1966 gives estimates for the future population of the United Kingdom for several years up to 2000, and from these we can calculate that the estimate for Great Britain for 1977, projected from the actual population in 1965, is about 59.8 millions. Demographers do not now purport to foretell the future; they merely give the results of exact calculations made from stated assumptions and, in order to emphasize this limitation, term these results 'projections' rather than 'forecasts'. Whether or not the more fundamental method gives a better result than relatively crude empirical methods for obtaining a single forecast on which political decisions can be based, it is more convincing and is certainly better for showing the effects of changes in the causes of population change.

Methods of forecasting the volume of business and trade have been on various levels between the scientific and the empirical, and results have been given, sometimes as single numerical forecasts, sometimes as a range within which the future value is expected to lie, and sometimes as a mere qualitative indication of the changes expected. In 1951 there was considerable interest in the probable demand for coal in Great Britain for about ten years ahead, partly for guiding the National Coal Board in its development policy. The total demand was analysed, estimates were made of the future of the parts by considering such things as the predicted increase in industrial production, in the efficiency with which fuel is utilized, and in the supply of alternative fuels. Forecasts made by different bodies from assumptions that seemed reasonable to the forecasters, were between 205 and 263 million tons. The actual consumption in 1965 was 182 million tons.

Sometimes it has been noticed or postulated that business activity at one time has been related to something that is measured at some previous time, and where this relation can be given theoretical support it is not unreasonable to assume that it will continue with little or no change, and on that basis to make a prediction. For example, quarterly figures of the value of houses for which plans have been passed by local authorities have an obvious importance as predictors for manufacturers of building materials. Fairly elaborate systems of equations for forecasting general business activity have been evolved along such lines, but they seem to be made for some months ahead rather than for years ahead.

Attempts to predict prices have also been based on the well-known theory that prices are dependent upon supply, among other things. To be able to measure the relation between supply and price for any commodity it is necessary (1) that both quantities should, for some time, have changed enough, (2) that supply should have been an important factor in causing changes in price compared with other factors, (3) that the relation between supply and price should have been fairly stable, and (4)—which is almost the same as (3)— that the conditions of supply (e.g. methods of manufacture) and of demand (e.g. the tastes or habits of consumers) should not have changed much. Articles like motor-cars and television sets obviously do not satisfy these conditions, but a number of primary products do to some degree, and moderately successful formulae have been obtained for predicting the prices for a few months ahead from a knowledge of the existing supply (e.g. crop) of commodities like cereals, cotton, and meat. Other factors affecting price have also been considered in the same way.

The man of affairs often needs to know how the demand for an article is related to its price—the elasticity of demand—before deciding on a price policy. One British Chancellor of the Exchequer increased the tax on sparkling wines without knowing what effect the increased price would have on consumption, and the reduction in consumption that occurred was so great that his estimate of yield was completely falsified. In 1933 the British Railways took the very bold step of reducing most passenger fares from $1\frac{1}{2}d.$ to $1d.$ a mile with a view to arresting the decline in revenue. Lacking knowledge of the elasticity of demand, that important decision had to be made in the hope that increased mileage demanded by the public would be more than the one-third by which fares were reduced; otherwise revenue would have decreased. This hope was, in the event, justified. The problem of estimating the elasticity of demand is exactly similar, statistically, to that of determining the relation between price and supply. The same conditions are necessary for its solution, and similar degrees of success have been attained for various kinds of commodities.

I have had no direct experience of business and economic forecasting, but from reading have gained the impression that its achievements have been useful though modest. Forecasters themselves do not claim that their forecasts are at the best more than rough approximations, and for some statisticians and economists the whole process is held in as low esteem as crystal-ball gazing. Nevertheless the process goes on and men of affairs seem to find the results of some use. The fascination of the subject is great and the practical need to make assessments of the future is compelling; work on forecasting will doubtless continue and we may expect that with increasing knowledge and experience methods will improve.

A second aspect of the role of statistics in affairs I wish to consider concerns the surveys that are now made of consumer markets and public opinion. One of the chief functions of industry is to provide the people with the things they need and desire, and there is a growing tendency among commercial concerns to embark on 'consumer research' in order to discover what the needs and desires of the people are—an activity which seems to be a department of advertising.

A little of this work takes the form of indirect statistical investigation to discover what factors influence consumers' demands. Mr. Mordecai Ezekiel in his book *Methods of Correlation Analysis* mentions some investigations made in the U.S.A. into the relation between the prices received for various products and their qualities. For example, it was found well before World War II that on the Boston (Massachusetts) market for asparagus, $38\frac{1}{2}$ cents extra per dozen bunches was received per extra inch of green in the stalk, 4 cents less per dozen bunches of given weight was received for every additional stick in the bunch (i.e. there was a preference for few thick sticks to many thin ones), and bunches with sticks of uniform thickness fetched higher prices than those with variable sticks. It is stated that the results 'have had a marked influence on the practices by the producers who supply the Boston market, and have led to further experimental investigation as to how to produce asparagus with desirable qualities'. Statistical investigations of these kinds are essentially applications of the methods of correlation.

Most consumer research, however, uses only elementary statistical methods. For example, localities may be compared for population and the consumption per head of (say) soap, as a preparation for a sales campaign in 'backward' areas; or districts may be compared for population and spending capacity as assessed from the occupations followed, with a view to discovering where it would be most profitable to 'push' the sales of refrigerators, washing-machines, or television sets.

In this field, sample surveys are much used. Before introducing a new brand of chocolates, one firm got a panel of girls to try chocolates with variously flavoured centres, and included the favourite flavours in the brand; and the preference of the public for the short-headed tooth-brush was discovered by a special sample inquiry that was made before introducing a new brand of that article. One large store has investigated the habits of a sample of its customers to discover which ones buy at the stores regularly, in which departments they buy, the kinds of goods ordered by telephone, and so on, the aim being to provide data on which to base sales and advertising policies.

Sample surveys are much used for measuring public opinion, and the reactions of people to various things. For example, in both Great Britain and the U.S.A. 'public opinion polls' publish frequently the results of surveys disclosing the numbers of people having different attitudes to political questions, an activity that reaches a peak of interest just before a general election. During the early years of the war the British people anxiously watched the development of the attitude of the American people to the war through the figures published by the Gallup Poll. The Audience Research Department of the British Broadcasting Corporation uses sample surveys to discover the tastes and habits of listeners and viewers. The British Social Survey in the years since the war has given government departments information on such subjects as the effects of various items of publicity, methods of heating homes, the demand of ex-service men and women for campaign medals, the expenditure of households on various types of food, and the living conditions of people whose names are on the waiting lists of local authorities for houses. Doubts have at times been expressed as to the advisability of frequently testing public opinion and publicizing the results; there have been fears that leaders would tend to follow opinion rather than to lead; fears have been expressed that the publication of the results of opinion polls during an election campaign may influence the way people vote in the election; and there has been perceived a potential danger in allowing sectional interests to have some of the very powerful knowledge that surveys can give. However, the doubts and fears seem to be dying down and these surveys are now accepted as a legitimate part of the scheme of things.

Two activities that have developed since the war are *input-output analysis* and *linear programming*. The first stage in input-output analysis involves the formation of a two-way table like Table 7 in which the first column classifies the output of an economy—coal, steel, textiles, radio products, and so on—and the first row classifies the sectors of the economy—say the industries of a country—for which the various classes of output specified in the first column are input. The entries in the table state the value of the various classes of output going to the various sectors. For example the table shows, by value, how the output of steel for a given year is distributed between the steel industry itself for internal construction, the railways, shipbuilding, building, and so on. Such a table, of course, only shows what has happened over a given period of time, but, with the aid of assumptions, it can be used to predict what will be the effect on other sectors of the economy of an increase in the activity of one, e.g. of an increase in the demand for armaments, and what will be the effects throughout the economy of a change in the supply of some class of output. So far, input-output analysis is being developed largely for countries and not for smaller economic units.

Linear programming is the name given to a special branch of the process of finding what combination of alternative resources produces the maximum profit or efficiency, or the lowest cost. Examples are (a) 'programming' the voyages for a fleet of ships, each of known tonnage, which are situated at certain ports; the objective is to move given cargoes between these and other ports at a minimum cost, and (b) deciding what blend of motor spirits having known performances and costs will produce the cheapest mixture having a specified performance. The programming is 'linear', and the mathematical formulation of the problem has characteristics that are 'linear', in the mathematical sense; and these characteristics give the processes of solution a special form. Linear programming is now a commonplace in industry.

Until World War II statistics was useful in affairs largely through the straightforward presentation of numerical information in tables and charts. Apart from experience, persistence and care were almost the only attributes required for the collection of the data and common sense for their interpretation. These attributes are still the most important of all, and the statistical information must still be presented in a form to be fully apprehended by administrators and executives who are not statisticians; but methods of analysis have tended to become more esoteric and there is now scope for expert statisticians of several kinds. The economical and expeditious handling of large masses of figures is a skilled job, requiring powers of organization and a knowledge of what can be done with the aid of the very expensive and intricate accounting and sorting machines that were available well before the war and of the more recently introduced electronic machines for processing data. These last are so speedy and powerful that they have transformed the handling of statistical data. In some fields, notably in that of national income measurement or social accounting, the quantities under measurement are difficult in conception and some have to be arbitrarily defined; some of the data are difficult to obtain and have to be derived indirectly; consequently expert knowledge is required to handle the information reliably. Further, correlation methods, the intricate calculations involved in 'taking account of chance' (Chapter 7) in business, and the ever extending use of sampling techniques require the services of expert statisticians. But the administrator and the statistician cannot work independently. That each must know something of the other's work is now recognized in training for the relevant professions and in the corresponding examination syllabuses.

11

Statistics and Other Sciences

IN THIS CHAPTER I consider the relations between statistics and other branches of knowledge, using the term science broadly to denote any department of knowledge based on observed facts. First I consider economics.

Sir John Hicks has likened economics to medicine in being divisible into an anatomy describing the structure of the body economic and a physiology describing its functioning. The 'anatomy' is indubitably the province of economic statistics, and Hicks uses it as a framework for accounting for national resources of wealth and the disposal of that wealth, i.e. the national income and outlay.

The place of statistics in the 'physiology' of economics is not so clear. There are three reasons why, at first sight, the subject would be expected to be closely dependent on statistics. First, the laws of economic change, if they exist, refer to mass or group phenomena. Economic events are the result of actions based on the preferences, desires, and reactions of millions of people. Individually, people behave in a way that is unpredictable—some would say in a way that is indeterminate, i.e. that people have 'free-will'—and if there are any regularities in their behaviour they are only shown in the behaviour of the mass, as described in Chapter 8.

It does not necessarily follow, of course, that because individual people bear superficial resemblances to statistical individuals, the mass must show statistical regularities in behaviour; but such regularities do in fact seem to exist. The laws of supply and demand, for example, apply very widely; and even in time of war, when patriotic sentiments are most powerful, the enforcement of regulations that run counter to those laws involves a continual battle against such forms of evasion as 'black markets'. The belief that statistical laws do in fact describe human behaviour is implicit in the very existence of the social sciences—including economics—and in a rational approach to all business, political, and social problems.

This belief does not necessarily carry with it belief in the permanence or universality of economic laws. For example, the reactions of men to financial incentives are conditioned by their ideology, which may change with time and place—the ideology of a group of Oriental mystics is very different from that of a group of English business-men. Nevertheless, we believe, and act as though we believe, that most economic events follow laws which are sufficiently stable and widely applicable to be useful.

If the behaviour of people in the mass, as manifested for example in the laws of economic change, is to be described in terms of the behaviour of the fundamental units—the individuals—statistical ideas and techniques must play an important part. An analogy may be seen in the description of some of the properties of matter in terms of the behaviour of the fundamental units: molecules, atoms, electrons, and so on. Very little progress in this direction has been made for the social sciences, but the detailed information about individuals derived from social surveys opens possibilities for the future.

A second reason for expecting economic science to be dependent on statistics (using the word as referring to numerical data) is that the scientific way of discovering laws involves studying what actually happens, and unless the knowledge so gained is quantitative, i.e. statistical, it is 'of a meagre and unsatisfactory kind'. The immense progress that has been made in the older and more exact sciences of physics and chemistry has depended very much on measurement, and, by analogy, one would expect the same condition of progress to apply to economics.

Thirdly, if laws are to be inferred from numerical data, this must be done by methods that are largely statistical, as opposed to experimental. Economic experiments purely for the sake of gaining knowledge are not allowed; and, even if they were, it would not often be possible to isolate a few factors for investigation as the experimentalist can in his laboratory. The consequence is that the economist can only learn by observing the events that happen outside his control.

Statistical data may be used in economic inquiries in three ways:

(1) they may give the information that suggests and leads to the formulation of theories, (2) they may be used for testing theories, and (3) they may provide measures of quantities that emerge from economic analysis.

(1) Economic changes can only be described by statistics, but the analysis of statistics does not seem to have played much part in suggesting economic theories. Jevons's famous suggestion that cyclical changes in prices are correlated with sunspots was based largely on an examination of data, but it did not have a very lasting effect on economic theory. The statistics of trade fluctuations have been studied considerably and doubtless the resulting information has affected the thinking of economists; but one cannot discover that economic analysis has been directly affected in the way, for example, that the theory of the electron was determined by J. J. Thomson's studies of the passage of electricity through gases. Articles in economic journals and economic books contain certain algebraic formulae with unevaluated constants and formal diagrams, but very little in the way of observational data. Lord Keynes wrote in 1933:

In economic discussions Ricardo was the abstract and *a priori* theorist, Malthus the inductive and intuitive investigator who hated to stray too far from what he could test by reference to the facts and his own intuitions. . . .

One cannot rise from a perusal of this correspondence [i.e between Malthus and Ricardo] without a feeling that the almost total obliteration of Malthus's line of approach and the complete domination of Ricardo's for a period of a hundred years has been a disaster to the progress of economics.

Nevertheless, Keynes himself, however much he referred back to the facts of economic life as a basis for his theories, did not seem to receive much help from statistics. In his book *The General Theory of Employment, Interest and Money*, for example, there are only three small statistical tables in 384 pages. In another place he refers to 'the amalgam of logic and intuition and the wide knowledge of facts, most of which are not precise, which is required for economic interpretation in its highest form'. The mind can deal with facts that are not precise, whereas the more formal methods of statistics cannot; and the volume of unprecise facts is enormous compared with that of precise facts. That may be one reason why qualitative analysis has gone so far without statistics. Another reason is probably that the economist is a man studying the behaviour of men; he sees the economic system from the inside. Further, the patient collection

and analysis of statistical data requires a different kind of tempera-
ment from that required for the development of economic theory.
People who are not economists have at times condemned the methods
of economists; I neither presume nor desire to do this. I think that
we may admire the high intellectual quality and penetrating
power of qualitative economic analysis, and acknowledge the success
it has achieved.

(2) Economic theories have, from time to time, been put to the
test by reference to statistics, but the results have not been very
impressive. The whole economic system is so complicated that it is
usually possible to suggest a number of theories to fit a given set of
statistical facts. Consequently, when theoretical predictions have
been compared with experience and there have been discrepancies,
the tendency has been, not to abandon or modify the theory, but
to find special reasons why the particular facts did not conform to
the theory. The following quotation from some remarks made in
1938 by Professor von Hayek illustrates the situation from the
standpoint of one economist:

He [Thomas Tooke] showed—and there can be little doubt about the fact—
that low rates of interest usually coincide with falling prices, and high
interest rates with rising prices, and concluded from this that the Ricardian
idea, that a reduction in the rate of interest would lead to a rise of prices
and vice versa, was wrong. I doubt whether there is to-day a single economist of repute who would be willing to assert for this reason, with Tooke,
that a low interest rate leads to a fall in prices or the contrary. I need hardly
waste time to explain the paradox—but statistical research has not helped
us in any way to solve the difficulty.

Tooke was presumably mistaking a correlation arising from
movements in the trade cycle for a causal relationship. A modern
statistician could correct for the effect of the trade cycle and obtain
a partial correlation between prices and the rate of interest; but
he could be reasonably sure that he had a true measure of a causal
relationship only if theoretical analysis supported that view.
Statistical analysis can separate the effects of various factors, given
sufficient data, but usually only after the factors are stated by theory.
Thus it seems that, in existing circumstances, theory inevitably
controls the analysis of observational data and is almost unaffected
by the results. It is not altogether unreasonable for economists to
cling to their theories in spite of discordant statistical facts which so
often are only *apparently* discordant.

In situations similar to this it is often profitable to take the theory for granted and to use the statistics to measure the importance in certain circumstances of the factors postulated in the theory. On this view, one would not have regarded Tooke's results as disproving the Ricardian idea altogether, but rather as showing that some other factor was having a much more important effect in causing the particular variations observed. The value of this viewpoint is greatest when the theoretical effects are important, but not all-important.

(3) Economic theory postulates a number of quantities such as the elasticity of supply and demand which appear only as algebraic symbols, but need to be evaluated if they are to be used. Such evaluation is a proper function of statistical methods working on statistical data. In the language of the relatively new subject of *econometrics* (the structure of the word discloses roughly the content of the subject), a mathematically formulated theory of the working of some part of the economic system is termed a 'model'; and it is the job of the econometrician to give the models numerical expression. I have already discussed the problem as far as the evaluation of the constants of supply and demand is concerned; it is only necessary to add here that econometrics is a very live subject and that much work is being done in it.

The connexion between statistics and the study of the functioning of the economic system has thus been less than might at first sight be expected, especially by anyone familiar with the working of the scientific method in the natural sciences. But the situation is changing. The volume and cogency of statistical information are increasing; valuable material and experience are being provided by the economic changes accompanying wars, slumps, and political revolutions; statistical methods of analysis are improving in power and flexibility and are becoming more discriminative; and statisticians and economists are gaining in skill and knowledge. How fundamentally these developments will affect economic method is yet to be seen, but we may expect that economics, and indeed all the social sciences, will more and more resemble the natural sciences in the way in which the advancement of knowledge is based on precise, observed facts.

The connexion of statistics with biology is traditionally almost as close as with economics. As long as biologists were concerned with merely describing organisms and their functions, and with classifying them into types, statistics did not come into the picture. When measurements began to be made, and the existence of variation to be recognized, statistical ideas and methods became necessary and many modern statistical methods were first developed for biological applications.

It was under the influence of Darwin's ideas and work that Galton started his numerical studies of biological variation and founded the Biometric Laboratory already referred to (p. 51). The main work of the biometricians during the early years of this century was the study of heredity in man, and of factors responsible for the 'deterioration' (as the trend was pessimistically characterized) of the race; but the scope inevitably broadened to include a variety of biological problems. This statistical approach to biology and statistical methods are twins, born and cradled together in the Biometric Laboratory.

The description of populations of biological individuals is statistical. The pages of early biometric papers abound in frequency distributions of the characters of men (height, weight, reaction times to sight and sound, and so on), of plants and flowers, and of animals; and there are association and correlation tables showing the statistical relationships between two or more characters, such as the weight and vital capacity of men, the numbers of pistils and stamens in flowers, and the heights of fathers and sons. The idea behind the phrase 'like father like son' is more exactly expressed as far as height is concerned by the statement that the correlation coefficient between the heights of fathers and sons is about $+0.5$.

The methods of statistics find their use in all branches of biology, including its applications. Applied psychologists, for example, emphasize the existence of 'individual differences' between people, but they are really calling attention to variation which they treat on ordinary statistical lines. A good deal of applied psychology is concerned with developing tests for intelligence, for skill of various kinds, for accident proneness, and so on; and the criterion of the value of such tests is that their results shall correspond with the performance of the individual in school or in some job. Such correspondence is never exact, however, so the problem of measuring its degree becomes one of statistical correlation. In this direction, psychologists have developed from the orthodox methods some variants of their own, to suit their special requirements.

Genetics is essentially a statistical subject, being concerned with the relations between the characters of groups of individuals in successive generations. The earlier work of the biometricians in this connexion was largely descriptive and empirical. This was perhaps necessary and inevitable in the early stages of the subject, and the knowledge gained has presumably been of value; but the work seems to have been almost sterile as far as the progress of genetics is concerned. A more fruitful line of attack has been based on theories developed from Mendel's discoveries. This has proceeded along statistical lines, and elaborate and highly developed statistical and mathematical methods now form the basis of a large and important branch of the subject.

Statistics is of importance in medicine. Vital statistics, epidemiology, and public health are rightly regarded as statistical since they are concerned with masses of people and are based on data that are conventionally thought of as statistical—death rates, sickness rates, and so on. Statistics is also useful in medical research. The medical records of patients are used to give information on the causes and effects operating in the world of health and disease and require sound statistical analysis if sound inferences are to be made. Drugs and treatments are tested for efficacy, and tests have to be properly designed and the results examined by statistical criteria if 'significant' results are to be obtained. Work in this field, incidentally, is rendered difficult by the limitations imposed by medical ethics—the welfare of the patients is the first consideration and the requirements of a scientific experiment are considered only within the framework set by that. Statistics is also as useful in the management of hospitals and other medical services as of other businesses. The general practitioner and consultant deal with patients as individuals and it might be thought that they have no need of statistics. But many medical generalizations that must be applied to the individual necessarily concern statistical populations of patients; the practitioner needs to be 'statistically minded' in order to be able to think of his patient as a member (sometimes an exceptional member) of that population. In this sense many doctors probably use statistical ideas without knowing it.

In agriculture, correlation methods have been used to determine, from observations on farms not under control, what factors influence such things as the quantity and quality of crops. Such investigations have included the measurement of the effects of rainfall, sunshine, and temperature on the yield of various crops; of the relation between variations from farm to farm of the gain in weight of cattle and the quantity and quality of food; and of similar relations between the fertilizers used and the yield of various crops. This kind of investigation seems to have been more characteristic of American than of English agricultural research. In England, farm surveys have been more concerned with agricultural economics, and investigations for improving products and yield have been largely experimental. The modern statistical methods of arranging experiments and making inferences from the results, described on pages 85–87, originated in agricultural experimentation.

These methods and the methods of sampling are essential to all quantitative experiments and investigations in all branches of biology, since biological material is inherently variable. There are also many routine biological tests of counts of bacteria in milk, of the germination of plant seeds, counts of blood particles, and so on; and the biological value of batches of substances like insulin is tested by measuring their effects on animals (e.g. rabbits) that differ in their individual reactions. In all these instances, two important questions have to be asked: 'What is the most economical way of arranging the tests to give an average result of required accuracy?' and 'How many tests must be made to attain this accuracy?' Statistical methods provide the answers, and it is only when the second of these questions has been properly answered that statements of, say, the vitamin content of various preparations can be relied upon, and substances like insulin can be reliably standardized.

A great revolution took place when statistical ideas were imported into physics and chemistry—particularly the former. Physics had always been regarded as dealing with invariable constants of nature, perfectly determinate and measured with great precision. Very little room for statistics there! The conception of matter as an aggregate of elementary particles—atoms—is an old one, and contained nothing statistical, since all the atoms were alike. When, however, the particles were given different characteristics the aggregate became a statistical population and the laws of its behaviour statistical laws. This happened first with the kinetic theory of gases, in which the molecules of a gas moved in different directions with different velocities, and now applies to the modern theories of matter in terms of electrons and the like. Indeed, it seems that the only way of visualizing the electron nowadays is as a kind of a blur of probabilities. The statistical approach is not often necessary if the physicist is interested only in the properties of matter in the mass, i.e. the behaviour of the aggregate of elementary particles, but it is when he attempts to relate such properties to observations on the elementary components.

Physicists have developed their own statistical methods almost independently of the work of statisticians in other fields—there is little in common between statistical mechanics and the kinds of statistics described in this book. It may be, however, that the two branches of the subject will be related one day. Certainly the ideas used are not unique to physics.

Statistical ideas have also some place in modern chemical theories. Chemists are attempting to explain the behaviour of substances like cellulose, rubber, and proteins by postulating aggregates or chains of molecules of different lengths and weights. Changes in the behaviour of the substance as a result of chemical change are explained in terms of changes in the frequency distribution of chain length.

In both physics and chemistry, measurements made in the laboratory are subject to experimental errors. Statistical methods are somewhat used for dealing with these, although, as I have stated in Chapter 7, this application is limited. Physicists and chemists increasingly have to make measurements on variable material, however, particularly since the development of biophysics and biochemistry and the extended use of physics and chemistry in industry. Moreover, it may sometimes be necessary in technical research to make investigations or test laboratory conclusions in factories. For a variety of reasons, perfectly controlled experiments are not possible in a factory, but some degree of experimental control can often be achieved without unduly upsetting the factory routine, and a statistical experiment can be arranged. Also, a statistical analysis of the records of physical and chemical tests on output and quality, that are often kept in factories as a routine, may sometimes suggest the existence of technical effects or the causes of unwanted variations. All these situations open a wide field for the application of statistical methods to sampling, arranging experiments, and analysing and testing the significance of results.

Meteorology is usually regarded as a physical subject, presumably because the causes of weather changes are physical, but the subject also has statistical characteristics. The meteorologist has no control over weather variations, and can only record and reduce them in much the same way that we do other statistical data, using frequency distributions, averages, correlations, and so on. Many of the meteorologist's diagrams are of a special character, however, since he may require to represent at the same time, say, the wind strength and direction at various stations measured at various times of the year. Weather forecasting is based on the same logical and mathematical principles and methods as business forecasting.

In engineering experience there exists that uncontrollable variation which always indicates a field for the application of statistics. The materials the engineer uses, both raw and manufactured, vary in strength, size, and quality; loads borne by his structures and machines vary (e.g. wind pressures, the amount of traffic on a bridge, the demand for electricity); and he is often unable to control all the working conditions, such as temperature or humidity, of the processes in his charge. Sometimes the variation is small absolutely, but must be considered because it is large compared with the precision that is required. Consequently, use must be made of frequency distributions, averages, measures of variation, and so on. For example, the strength of metal specimens is related to their hardness, and since the strength test is destructive and the hardness test is not, this relationship is of value. It is not exact, however, but is a statistical correlation, and should be regarded and treated as such. Also, sampling problems are raised in many engineering tests of materials and articles.

Engineers have their own ways of taking account of variation, but they are not always the best ways. To allow for variations in materials and loads, engineers use a factor of safety when designing a machine or structure, making the parts several times as strong as they would need to be if they all had the average strength and had always to bear the average load. These safety factors are empirical— they have been referred to as factors of ignorance—whereas it is theoretically possible to calculate them from the statistics of the variations. Such calculations have difficulties, but developments in this direction should be possible, and would almost certainly be profitable.

Another engineering way of treating variation that is not always adequate is by the use of tolerance limits. Articles delivered to a specification are not expected to be all exactly alike, but are accepted

if, and only if, they are within certain tolerance limits of the specification. Tolerance limits are suitable in specifications for operations
like machining, where it is easy, with care, to keep within such limits
as are technically desirable, or where every article in each batch is
inspected and those outside the limits can be separated and rejected.
But if the inspection is by sample, the rigid use of tolerance limits
involves the rejection of a whole batch if even one article in the sample
is outside them, although the very fact that a sample is used implies
the possibility of accepting a batch in which some articles are outside
the limits but none of them happened to come in the sample. It is
illogical to be willing to run this risk and yet to reject another batch
because one or two articles in its sample happen to come outside the
limits. Such a rejection may also be uneconomic, or it may lead to
tolerance limits that are too wide to be of value. For example, limits
for the life of electric lamps would have to be set at (1) a little above
zero and (2) 3,400 hours, if the batch represented by the sample of
Table 5 (p. 35) is to be accepted! And a batch in which all lamps had
lives between, say, 200 and 500 hours would satisfy a specification
containing such limits equally with a batch with lives between, say,
200 and 3,400 hours. It is important to specify not only the allowable
limits of variation, but also the proportions of articles in the different
regions between those limits.

The movement for the application of statistics in engineering is
part of the general movement for applying the subject to technical
control and research in industry. Engineers have not generally
regarded themselves as needing statistical methods, but in recent
years an increasing number have realized how useful the methods
may be, and have applied them. Moreover, there is a growing
tendency to recognize statistical quality control (p. 126) as an
engineering subject.

Statistics finds occasional application to many subjects. In literature, for example, frequency distributions of the lengths of sentences
have been used to characterize one aspect of the style of authors.
A striking and most interesting statistical investigation in the literary
sphere is a study of Shakespeare made by Caroline F. E. Spurgeon
and described in her book *Shakespeare's Imagery*. She presented tables
of the frequencies of various types of images used by Shakespeare in
five of his plays and in certain writings of Bacon and other contem-
poraries. In the preface to her book, Spurgeon wrote:

Shakespeare's images have, of course, constantly been picked out and drawn upon, to illustrate one aspect or another of the poet's thought or mind, but the novelty of the procedure I am describing is that *all* his images are assembled, sorted, and examined on a systematic basis.

She also asserted that: '. . . in the case of a poet . . . it is chiefly through his images that he, to some extent unconsciously, "gives himself away".'

Spurgeon reached one conclusion, among others: that there are two minds behind the works of Shakespeare and Bacon.

Part of geography is concerned with the numerical description of facts of population, trade, manufactures, crops, and so on of different areas—that is to say with statistics in the ordinary understanding of the term. Statistical description and analysis, and sampling, are also used in geology in studying the distribution of fossils, the particle sizes of deposits of rocks, and so on.

Statistical data for past years are also part of the raw material of history. For example, the statement 'The Reform Act of 1832 had little immediate impact on either the social composition of the House of Commons or the legislation which it passed', which was made in a newspaper article by a historian, can only be demonstrated by a statistical study of the members of the House of Commons and of the Acts they passed before and after the Reform Act. In investigating English Local Government the Webbs used sampling methods for studying local Acts of Parliament passed between 1689 and 1834. Social facts of the sixteenth and seventeenth centuries are adduced by reconstructing families and family histories from parish records. Historians are thus becoming conscious of the help the statistical approach can give them.

Statistical methods are also used in examining the results of psychical experiments. Such experiments are usually so arranged that their results cannot be explained by what we regard as natural causes, but require a psychical explanation if they are not attributable to chance. For example, a pack of cards may be shuffled and then turned up one at a time by an operator; a subject who cannot see the cards states to what suit each one belongs; if he is right he scores *one* and if not he scores *nothing*. The question then arises: is the subject's score greater than can be attributed to chance? i.e. is it greater than it would have been had he guessed the cards? The answering of such a question involves a regular use of standard statistical methods.

For some subjects statistics provides ideas of basic importance; for some it provides methods of investigation. In one way or the other, or in both ways, statistics has an impact on most other branches of knowledge. In this respect it is not unlike arithmetic. Arithmetic is so woven into the fabric of our thinking that we use it almost subconsciously, and, after leaving school, most of us are scarcely conscious of its existence as a separate department of study. On the other hand, most people are scarcely conscious of statistics except as a separate subject. I look forward to the day when statistics will occupy a place in education only a little way behind arithmetic; when everyone will learn as much of the subject as is necessary for ordinary life and for his particular vocation. Then everyone will use statistics easily and naturally, and such general introductory books as this will become obsolete.

Notes on Books

THE FOLLOWING is a selection from the many books that are available:

BACKGROUND READING

My Apprenticeship by Beatrice Webb. The life and work of a social investigator.

The Nature of Statistics by W. Allen Wallis and Harry V. Roberts. A paperback originating in the U.S.A.

'APPRECIATION' BOOKS

The Social Framework by J. R. Hicks. About the national income.

Economic Control of Quality of Manufactured Products by W. A. Shewhart. Still worth reading although published in 1931.

Technological Applications of Statistics by L. H. C. Tippett.

A Guide to Operational Research by W. E. Duckworth. Covers the application of statistical as well as other techniques.

Planning of Experiments by D. R. Cox.

INTRODUCTORY TEXTBOOKS FOR PARTICULAR
FIELDS OF APPLICATION

Survey Methods in Social Investigation by C. A. Moser.

Principles of Medical Statistics by A. Bradford Hill.

Statistical Methods for Chemists by W. J. Youden.

Psychological Statistics by Quinn McNemar.

Statistical Analysis in the Geological Sciences by R. L. Miller and J. S. Kahn.

Statistical Quality Control by Eugene L. Grant.

Essentials of Quality Control by Alan Huitson and Joan Keen.

COMPREHENSIVE TEXTBOOKS

Facts from Figures by M. J. Morony.

Statistics by A. R. Ilersic.

Statistics in Theory and Practice by L. R. Connor and A. J. H. Morrell.

An Introduction to the Theory of Statistics by G. Udny Yule and M. G. Kendall.

SOURCES OF ECONOMIC AND COMMERCIAL STATISTICS

Chapters in the last two books above.

Government Statistical Services. A pamphlet issued by H.M. Stationery Office.

Statistics of the British Economy by F. M. M. Lewes. A survey, mostly of official statistics, that was up to date in 1966.

Index